AIR RIDERS' WEATHER

Alan Watts

A & C Black · London

First published 1992 by
A & C Black (Publishers) Limited
35 Bedford Row, London WC1R 4JH

ISBN 0 7136 3570 3

A CIP Catalogue record for this book is available from the British Library.

Designed by Rowan Seymour
Set in 10/11½ pt Ehrhardt Monophoto by
August Filmsetting, St Helens
Printed and bound in Great Britain by
Butler & Tanner Ltd, Frome and London

CONTENTS

ILLUSTRATIONS
The colour plate section appears between pages 58 and 59

ACKNOWLEDGEMENTS

At the outset I would particularly like to thank Peter Williams of Sailwings, Northney Marina, Hayling Island, Hants for suggesting that I write this book and also for his help and encouragement along the way. Also, my thanks are due to the staff of Sky Systems, Edburton, W. Sussex BN5 9LL for all their help with photographs.

Figs 6.3 and 6.4 are based on Brunt's *Weather Study*.

Fig. 6.6 is based on a diagram in *Wind and Sailing Boats* by Alan Watts (David & Charles, 1973).

Fig. 6.8 is after 'The Vertical Profile of the Mean Wind Velocity in the Surface Layers of the Atmosphere' by E. L. Deacon (Porton Technical Paper No. 39).

Figs 7.4 and 7.5 are based on 'The Structure of Wind Over Level Country' by M. A. Giblet and others (*Geophysical Memoir*, No. 54, Meteorological Office).

Fig. 8.4 is based on 'Measurements and predictions of flow and turbulence over an isolated hill of moderate slope' by Mason and King (Quart, J. Roy, Met. Soc. 111).

Fig. 8.5 is based on 'Some Weather Patterns in Snowdonia' by D. E. Pegley (*Weather*, October 1971).

Fig. 8.7 is after 'Wave Currents on the Leeward Side of Mountain Crests' (*Bull. met. tchecosl*, Prague, 1949).

Fig. 8.10 is after 'Zur theorie der Hangewinde, nebst Bemerkungen zur Theorie derBerg and Talewinde' by Defant (*Arch. Met.*, Wien, 1949).

Fig. 8.12 is from *Basic Windcraft* by Alan Watts (David & Charles).

Figs 11.4 and 11.5 are based on *Hazards in Mountaineering* by Pauleke and Dumler (Kaye and Ward, 1973).

Fig. 12.4 is based on 'Wind-tunnel Studies of Shelter Belt Models' by Woodruf and Zingy (*Washington Journal of Forestry*, 51, 1953).

Fig. 13.2 is after *Meteorological Magazine*, June, 1962 (G. J. Bindon).

Fig. A3 is from *Wind and Sailing Boats* by Alan Watts (David & Charles, 1973).

A number of the figures in Part 2 are from *Reading the Weather* by Alan Watts (Adlard Coles, 1987).

Fig. D.1 is from *Weather Forecasting Ashore and Afloat* by Alan Watts (Adlard Coles).

Fig. W.2 is after 'Physiological climates of the conterminous United States; a biological classification based on man' by W. H. Terjung (*Amat. Ass. Amer. Geogr.*, 56, 1966).

Photograph C.2 is by Jacqui Belcher.

Photograph P.2 is by Audrey Gilkes.

Photograph R.1 is reproduced courtesy of the Meteorological Office, Radar Research Laboratory, Malvern.

Photograph 12.1 is by Peter Spinlove.

Photograph 13.1 is by Laurie Dent.

The cloud satellite studies are by the Satellite Receiving Station at Dundee University.

All the photographs other than those mentioned are by the author.

ABOUT THIS BOOK

This book is aimed at those hang glider and paraglider pilots who may often be 'doing their own thing' and who need help with the met. side of their sport. However, it is hoped balloon pilots will find most of their weather needs covered here also, as all these 'air riders' greatly depend on the wind and the weather.

Powered hang gliders and paragliders are appearing in increasing numbers, but their engine capacities are such as to leave even these still very much at the mercy of the weather. So, the information given here should be of use to the pilots of all those microlight aircraft which are continuing to populate the skies. Also, because *Air Riders' Weather* looks at the attributes of that first few thousand feet of air-deck in which most gliders will fly, it should be useful to sailplane pilots, too. I have called all the inhabitants of the Earth's boundary layer 'air riders' and have looked at weather, wind and air motion as it affects them.

As well as the chapters on winds and weather, there is also some necessary explanation of gliding. It is important to realise the limitations of a wing, sail or parafoil so that you do not fly in conditions that will put you in unnecessary danger. Not that danger isn't there. If you sail a boat, the furthest you can fall is a few feet and then you land in something soft – water! With gliding, if all you have to fall is a few feet, then you are not gliding and the last thing you want to fall into is the sea – or any water. Any accidents bring you down to earth with a bump and so gliding is potentially more dangerous than other comparable sports – which is where a great deal of its appeal comes from.

The air is a complex medium in which to exist. You only have to read the exploits of those in the past who have tried to glide to realise that. We now know much more about everything than the ancient aeronauts did – which makes it harder! There is so much more to be taken in and most pilots do not wish to be met. people. They want to know – or be able to make reference to – those things that will keep them safe and flying, and will avoid problems which are likely to ground them. To that end this book is written.

By means of the ready-reference tables the pilot ought to be able to come to grips with some of the complex weather events. A case in point is seabreezes. Many light aviation books mention seabreezes and then go on to a different subject, and yet most of the research into seabreezes has been done by glider pilots. Some of these were also meteorologists and I have been privileged to know a few of them and to do a little to help their work. Part of the work on seabreezes I undertook was to aid yachtsmen, but it is also useful to glider pilots: I have tried to tabulate helpful clues about when and if your site might conceivably be visited by a sudden wind from seaward when previously it was enjoying a wind in almost the opposite direction.

While they are important, seabreezes are just a small part of the phenomena that are found in the air and that affect gliding. However, they are an example of what you will find covered in detail in this book that may not appear in other texts. Those are often books about flying which have some reference to met. This, on the other hand, is a book about met. with some necessary references to flying. I hope you will find it authoritative but at the same time not stuffy; if it keeps some air riders safer than they might otherwise be, then it will have achieved its purpose.

Part I

I
THE PERFECT SITE

It is one of those days that air riders dream of. The hills roll softly away in both directions athwart the direction of the wind which blows gently up the grassy slope – a slope that looks a long way down towards fields where a landing would be easily possible if needed in a hurry. Over in the river valley to the right the smoke from a factory chimney bends upwards at forty-five degrees or so and shows no sign of sinking back. You know from experience that that means the wind is somewhere around 8kts, and the rising plume shows the air to be in a mood to rise rather than to sink. Not that you need smoke to tell you about that, for there are puffs of cotton-wool cloud gathering about the sky showing where thermals are growing to feed them.

Before long the air is populated by the brightly coloured sails of hang gliders and the wings of paragliders. Once up, they gyrate in lazy circles, looking for the sustenance that comes both from the dynamic lift of the wind blowing up the slope and from the thermal currents generated by the sun. Nearby newcomers from the local 'schools' that specialise in training air riders make their instructor-assisted hops and get the adrenalin flowing with their first real solo flights. There is something for everyone when you have found the perfect site on a perfect day.

When things seem this good it is easy to be lulled into a false sense of security. You take off and may forget that the day can change. You will have listened to your instructors at the school where you have learned the basics and, being as yet only an intermediate pilot, will fly within your limits. That was why you started to fly early while the wind was still light and before the thermals had really begun to develop. Keeping well in the lift band of the ridge, you stay up for a long time as lift continues to get better. Then all of a sudden you find that the wind has increased and you are having to stand out further from the ridge to avoid being blown back over it during your figure- of-eight perambulations. The wind was not quite up the slope when you took off but was certainly within the recommended thirty-degree angle of dead straight on. You look around for some sign of why the school has abandoned its training hops and find that the wind has shifted as well as increased, making a landing on your take-off point hazardous. The wind increase and shift have brought the wind tumbling over and round a grove of trees that were previously not affecting take-off, so there are going to be turbulent eddies where you wanted to land back by your gear. You have to look for somewhere else and you are worried by the change in conditions. Other-wise the day looks OK. The sun still shines, although the cloud cover has increased but doesn't look threatening.

What you have experienced happens on most days when flying looks like being idyllic. It is caused by the breaking of the inversion layer that forms through the night when weather conditions are fine. Before the layer breaks, thermal currents are inhibited and the wind above is cut off from the wind below. Then the thermals develop enough to punch through the inversion and the wind up there comes down onto the surface. The wind will immediately shift direction as well as increase in speed. Once the inversion breaks, up-and-down thermal currents strengthen and, should you get into a persistent down current, you can lose height very rapidly.

This is just one example of how a perfectly normal weather event, which happens very regularly, may make problems for you when you have found what you imagine is the perfect site. Another is when you fly a ridge within some 30 miles (50km) of the main coastline. Say your slope lies 20 miles (33km) from a south-facing coast and looks west.

Although your chosen slope may not fully get the sun at this early hour, dynamic lift keeps you up until thermals develop. There is a nice gentle westerly wind during the morning, which increases a little but not much. You come down for lunch, determined not to lose a minute of this great day and to get into the air again as soon as possible. Now that the sun is shining fully on your site, thermals are producing fleets of fair-weather cumulus, making for very good lift.

You are so engrossed in flying that you do not notice how the sky has become much brighter over towards the south and that a deeper, darker line of cloud is approaching from that direction. The line has odd-looking 'curtains' of ragged cloud hanging below it in places, quite different from the nice hard bases of the rest of the cumulus (Cu) that is around. Soon you see why the southern sky is so bright. There is next-to-no cloud there. The cloud-line moves inexorably over you and you are suddenly aware of much stronger lift. It is too strong! You increase sink to counteract it. Down below, you see that the wind, which was west, is now south. It is blowing along the ridge and making landing a real problem. Still you stay flying into the unbroken sunshine as the cloud wall of what is actually a seabreeze front moves on inland. Now, despite the sun, you find you are losing much of your lift. You are coming down in the sinking air which always exists on the seaward side of a seabreeze front. You have to make some quick decisions and so find a landing site which is into wind but nowhere near your original take-off point. That means a long hike to find your support.

Just another example of a regular occurrence, say, on the south or east coasts of England where seabreeze fronts penetrate up to 50 miles (80km) inland, although they will only arrive at such distances well into the evenings of May or June. A mere 20 miles (33km) inland you can easily come across the scenario painted above and should allow for it when the conditions are right.

But how do you know when the conditions are right? The seabreeze is rather a complex wind system and you are not a meteorologist. That is why pages such as 95 (What chance of a seabreeze?) are a feature of this book and, when you have to think about your flight plan for the day, you should consult them. They will help you ask the right questions and so you can plan accordingly.

In the following pages there will be found tables which will help you assess the likelihood of these and other weather-related events occurring. The events may not take place, but at least you have been warned that they might. Ordinary weather forecasts cannot be relied on to give you the detailed information you need. Neither should you depend on aviation forecasts for light aircraft, because the pilots tend to fly above your air-deck anyway. Also, the peripatetic paraglider pilots who hike off into the hills with their wings on their back can be out of touch with such information.

If you come across words and phrases about whose meaning you are unsure or on which you need more information look them up in the alphabetical reference section in Part 2.

Sailplane pilots will find much of use to them here, even though the book is primarily intended for non-rigid-glider pilots. The seabreeze and local hill or mountain wind information is important to any glider, rigid-winged or not. Sailplanes will, by their nature, be largely restricted to airfields where pilots have the facilities to get them in to the air. These will often have quite advanced meteorological instrumentation, and weather information may well come via weather facsimile so that charts are readily available. Even so, the information has to be interpreted and allowance made for local wind effects that will not be obvious from the official forecasts.

Of all aerial craft the balloon is the most weather-dependent. If the wind blows the wrong way, there is no turning back. You either go with it or land. A balloon is part of the air in which it finds itself and if that air becomes turbulent the balloonist can be in real trouble. The up and downdraughts near and under cumulus clouds can be a source of great concern to the balloon crew.

The perfect site for the balloonist is a big grass field sheltered by a deep belt of tall trees. Downwind there will be nothing nasty like electricity pylons or other extensive belts of trees. However, unlike the glider pilot, the balloonist will not be coming back to his take-off point, so he also hopes for a perfect landing place as well.

2

FACTS ABOUT THE AIR

Whatever you may fly, you have only the air to sustain you and so knowing about its normal behaviour is very important – your life may depend on it!

The atmosphere

The normal state of pressure and temperature in the atmosphere is as follows:
(a) pressure – decreases with height
(b) temperature – decreases with height
(c) density – decreases with height.

Pressure is due to the weight of air standing above any surface over which the pressure is to be measured and it varies normally from a value of 950 millibars (mb) in low pressure centres to 1050mb in the most intense anticyclones. These are only useful limits and it is not unusual to have Atlantic lows whose central pressures are below the magic figure of 950mb.

The met. services deal with a series of standard pressure levels of which 1000mb is near the ground. Above this we have standard levels at 850, 700, 500, 300, 200 and 100mb. It is useful to relate these falling pressures to the heights at which they normally occur, but it must be stressed that on any particular day the heights vary considerably.

TABLE 2.1 STANDARD PRESSURE LEVELS

1000mb	*360ft*
850	4800
700	10000
500	18000
300	30000

This table only shows the way the atmosphere normally behaves, but it is a good guide.

The 500mb level is a standard level used by the Met. services for global and other upper air charts of wind and temperature, but similar charts for all the standard levels are produced by the Met. services and are broadcast on radio weather facsimile. Anyone who has a suitable radio receiver, decoder and printer can obtain these and many other weather charts of actual and forecast surface and upper level weather. Met. forecasting stations attached to major airfields will receive similar but more detailed and extensive information by land line.

The 850mb level is around the tops of fair weather cumulus clouds when they first form in the morning, but it may be near their bases as the latter rise through the afternoon.

The 700mb level is a typical pressure at the level of altocumulus and altostratus clouds, i.e. the levels of the middle clouds in the atmosphere, although these can also easily exist at 500mb.

The 300mb level is the height of ice-crystal clouds (cirrus and cirrostratus) and is the highest useful level to which we need to go (see fig. 2.1).

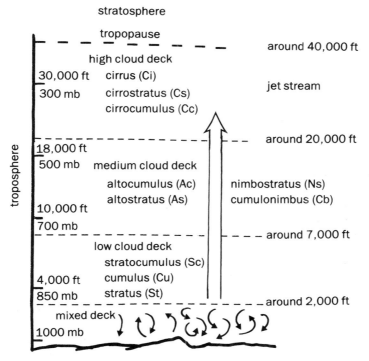

Fig. 2.1 The 'decks' of the troposphere

Because it is the norm for temperature to fall with height, in the real atmosphere there are layers where the temperature remains constant (isothermal layers) or actually increases (inversions) with ascent. The way in which the air changes its pressure temperature and humidity with height (the 'environmental lapse rate' or ELR) is measured twice a day by radiosonde balloons.

All over the world at midnight and midday GMT radiosonde ascents are made. A space denizen looking at this event will see a sudden 'cloud' of balloons being released at these two precise times, no matter what the local time may be. For example, on the eastern seaboard of the United States the balloons will be released at 7 a.m. and 7 p.m., as they are 5 hours back on GMT.

The results are plotted by meteorologists on special charts called 'tephigrams', but they can also be plotted as simple height against temperature graphs, and such a plot gives the 'environment curve' for the upper air at the time in question. It is this environment curve which shows the true way in which the air changes its temperature with height, and an example is shown in fig. 7.2. We will see in chapter 7 how this relates to the way air parcels (thermals) rise and cool and explain why the Cu (and other) clouds have the bases and tops that they do.

The troposphere

All weather processes are confined below an invisible layer called the 'tropopause'. Here the normal fall in temperature pauses and air cannot go on rising (see fig. 2.2). It is a permanent isothermal layer and its height may be 50,000ft over the tropics in summer, falling to 30,000ft over the polar regions. The only way that the tropopause can be 'seen' is when the 'anvils' of thunder heads are formed by the air spreading out sideways as it comes up against the tropopause.

The air-deck below the tropopause is called the 'troposphere' and all weather processes which are worth mentioning occur in the troposphere. We might define the 40,000ft depth of the troposphere as the 'weather zone'.

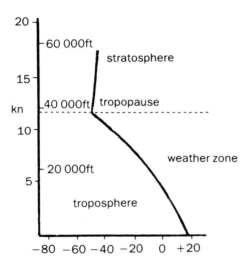

Fig. 2.2 The troposphere is where the air temperature falls with height and is where 'weather' occurs. The height of the tropopause varies with the season and with the airmasses below it. The stratosphere is characterised by having no great change of temperature with height

Humidity and dewpoint

The degree of wetness of the air, i.e. its humidity, is of very great importance. Any parcel of air will contain a certain quantity of water vapour, but this amount is limited by the temperature of the air parcel. Warm air can hold a greater quantity of water vapour than cold air can. If an air parcel rises in the atmosphere, it must cool and its temperature therefore gets closer and closer to the dewpoint temperature. The dewpoint is the temperature at which this parcel of air must begin to condense some of its water vapour into water droplets, i.e. it must form cloud or fog. The dewpoint depends on how much water vapour is contained in a kilogram of dry air and the amount of water vapour in the kilogram will be measured in grams. The more water vapour in the air, the higher the dewpoint temperature but it will always be less than the air temperature except when fog or cloud form.

So, the dewpoint is the temperature to which you have to cool an air parcel before it will form cloud or fog. Natural ascent reduces air to its dewpoint to form cloud, but ground fog is formed by wet air being cooled by the surface beneath it. In hilly areas a humid airstream (often from a southwesterly point) will be cooled by being pushed up the windward slopes and will form orographic cloud which may appear to be fog but is, in fact, cloud with its base on the ground (see Humidity, pp. 6–7).

Density is the mass (or amount) of air in unit volume and it varies with temperature, with height and with the amount of water vapour the air contains.

Cold air will be denser than warm air and wet air will be less dense than dry air.

Think of a large box whose sides are each a metre long. The air in the box is mainly molecules of nitrogen and oxygen plus some trace gases, such as CO_2, which can be neglected. At a fixed temperature the box can only hold so many molecules. If there are water vapour molecules in the air, they must occupy the space of air molecules, but water molecules weigh less than either oxygen or nitrogen so the whole mass of the mixture goes down. Thus the density of wet air is lower than that of dry air.

It is air density – or at least the changes in it – which gives an aerofoil lift. The lift forces come from the constant collision of the molecules with the aerofoil surfaces. Stretch the air over the top surface of the aerofoil and it becomes less dense. So, fewer molecules hit the top surface per unit time than the bottom surface. The result is an upward force – lift.

All this means that there is less lift when the humidity is high. Couple that with high altitude and the result is possibly an inability on the part of paragliders to get into the air without the aid of some opposing wind. High humidity also entails any glider flying faster to maintain an optimum rate of sink.

Lapse rates

Air parcels that ascend cannot cool at an arbitrary rate. There are just two fixed rates at which air can cool. One applies to when the air is 'dry', i.e. at a temperature above its dewpoint, and the other applies to air that has condensed its water vapour into cloud. For reasons that are not really important to explain at this moment the physical process by which the air cools is termed 'adiabatic' and the fall of temperature with height is called a 'lapse rate'. Thus we have:

(1) the **Dry Adiabatic Lapse Rate (DALR)** which is always 3°C for each 1000ft of ascent. This applies all the time the air is below the cloudbase

(2) the **Wet Adiabatic Lapse Rate (WALR)** which is roughly half that value, i.e. 1.4°C per 1000ft of ascent when the air is ascending in cloud.

The simple reason why the air cools more slowly when it ascends through cloud is that it is continually condensing its water vapour. This process of condensation releases so-called 'latent heat' which slows the rate of cooling. These ideas will be raised again in chapter 7 which looks at how cumulus clouds form and why they sometimes only grow moderately deep while at other times they stream off up to great heights and produce heavy showers or thunderstorms.

Wind

Wind, fairly obviously, is air in motion and we often do not have to seek the reason for that motion. You have a gentle wind from the west and no one asks, 'What started this wind?'. You just use what nature sends you. However, there are local winds, such as seabreezes and mountain and valley winds which start up because of local factors that you may be able to predict more or less accurately. You need to understand the mechanism of these, but the origins of large-scale winds, that are due to the prevailing pattern of lows and highs, troughs and ridges, will not be explained in any great detail. Here are the facts.

Winds near the surface blow roughly in the direction of the isobars on the weather map unless some local wind intervenes (see fig. 2.3). The surface wind blows at an angle out of high pressure into low. Sinking air in highs, therefore, can feed rising air in lows. The return path is effected at high altitude. The arrows along the isobars in fig. 2.3 show the 'gradient wind' which is the wind just above the mixed layer (see below).

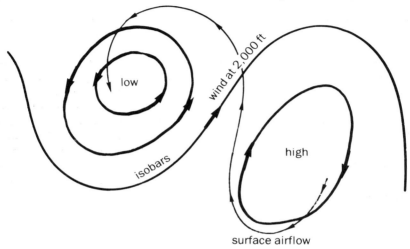

surface airflow

Fig. 2.3 Air sinks over high pressure regions and rises over low pressure ones. The winds at the surface must therefore blow out of high into low. The isobars define the wind at around 2000ft

Because paragliding, hang gliding and ballooning are limited to relatively low wind speeds the chances of the prevailing wind being changed out of all recognition by a local wind are quite large. So, look at the table on page 30. Add to this the fact that gliding is done off slopes, bluffs and cliffs around and over which the wind has to flow, and the air rider is more likely than most to meet strange winds that the forecast did not mention (see table on page 31). It is on days without much sunshine that the forecast wind is most likely to turn up unmodified by local influences. However, these are often not good for flying as one wants the assistance of thermals to reduce the rate of sink.

The important thing for glider pilots is that the wind should blow within an angle of 30° either side of the direction which is straight on to the slope from which they are flying. If it does they can fly – some experts may be able to fly outside these limits, but the above is a good general rule. If the wind direction at a particular moment is wrong, what things can change it to a more suitable direction? Or, if the direction is OK now, will a wind shift come along and make flying from here impossible? To prompt some questions and suggest some answers to this difficulty see the tables on pages 30–6.

Wind structure

The wind constantly collides with trees, houses, vegetation and objects of all kinds, and so becomes full of eddies (see fig. 2.4). These eddies are known as 'turbulence', and they are

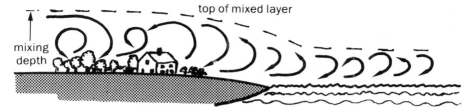

Fig. 2.4 The mixing depth depends on the roughness of the terrain in stable conditions. The sea is very smooth compared with the land and so the coast is a zone of transition

aided by thermals and suppressed by temperature inversions. They are bigger over the land than they are over the sea and sometimes, especially in the evening or early morning, they almost disappear and the air flows as it does over an aircraft wing – in laminar flow.

The turbulent layer is mixed by warm air parcels being lifted to higher regions while cool parcels are brought down. For this reason it is also called the mixed layer, and its depth is the mixing depth. The way the mixing alters the fall in temperature with height is shown in fig. 2.5. The mixed layer is also often called the Earth's 'boundary layer', because it is where the wind speed increases from zero on the ground to its unfettered speed clear of the Earth's clutter. The wind also develops gusts and lulls whose patterns may take minutes to pass as opposed to the turbulent eddies which pass in matters of seconds.

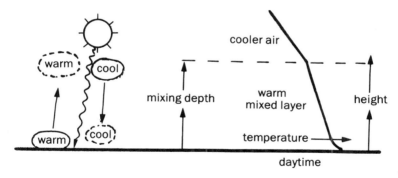

Fig. 2.5 Diagram showing how convection lifts warm parcels to higher levels and correspondingly brings cool air down. The mixed layer therefore becomes warmed during the day. The fall in temperature with height may become superadiabatic (curve of the temperature plot near the ground) during the middle of the day

The depth of the boundary layer is given for various wind speeds and for normal and stable conditions on page 48. Above this layer the wind may also change direction, but how it does so will depend on the local pattern of temperature in the air at its level. You will need intelligence from a Met. station to tell you what the upper wind directions are unless you can observe the motion of clouds at the levels you hope to reach. Normally glider flights will only be within the first few thousand feet and this is often not much deeper than the boundary layer anyway.

Effects of hills and mountains

Wind has to blow over hills and mountains, and where it cannot do so it has to blow round them. Both the process of blowing over and blowing round may have important bearing on gliding. The wind will particularly blow round obstructions when it is confined below an inversion of temperature. Inversions are most prevalent during the night, so the wind may pick up from odd directions in the evening which are different from the day-time ones and which are not what the forecast indicated. Equally, in the morning, before the sun has had a chance to warm the ground fully, the wind direction may not be the one forecast, but it is more likely to become that direction as the day progresses. Things are further complicated by the fact that air which blows over hill and mountain ridges develops immense waves. That these are in being can often be recognised when lens-shaped clouds form (see photographs 16 and 17). Extra care has to be exercised when flying in these 'wave-streaming' conditions.

Summary

This chapter has covered some of the more important aspects of the atmosphere as it affects gliders. All of these topics will be returned to in greater detail in the following chapters.

TABLE 2.2 THE MEANINGS OF CLOUDS AND SKIES

When you go into elevated places to look for the perfect site you need to keep an eye on the sky. This can keep you clear of imminent danger or modify your flight plan either for today or tomorrow.

Cloud type or situation	Previous history	Cloud	Wind/visibility now	Expect/advice	Thermal/dynamic lift
(1) Cirrus (Ci) often above cumulus (Photo 1)	Fair weather	Like Photo 1 when really bad weather is on the way. Advancing quickly from a W or NW point and increasing with time. Other forms are hooks and sheaves but speed of movement tells of bad weather	Light to moderate, maybe falling light and backing towards south/good to exceptional	A warm front with increasing and backing wind. Rain in some hours' time/make the most of it!	Probably has been good but advancing Ci will cut it off/increasing later and from a southerly point
(2) Cirrostratus (Cs) with a halo about the sun (Photo 2)	Increasing Ci as in (1). Cumulus fragments and dies or sometimes spreads into stratocumulus	Like Photo 2 with maybe some lens-shaped lower clouds. Not always with linear Ci as in the photo. Ahead of worst weather it is a milky veil across the sky	Backing and increasing/still very good	Coming weather to be due to an active depression. So possible gales later/time to pack up and go home?	Not much left by now/increasing now or expect soon
(3) Altostratus (As) (Photo 3)	Should follow (1) and (2) but often seen with lesser fronts	Like Photo 12 in hilly areas when it first appears but appears more like Photo 3 when rain is imminent	Should be from somewhere between SE and SW and increasing/poorer but still reasonable	When (1) (2) and (3) follow you certainly have a front on your hands and the low to go with it most times/past the time to pack up and go home	None left and probably sinking air/will become increasingly turbulent
(4) Nimbostratus (Ns) (Photo 4)	Follows (1) (2) and (3) when warm fronts and occlusions arrive. See (10) for cold fronts	Low stratus (pannus) below main cloudbase. Rain falls from high up. Covers slopes and tops (Photo 4)	Can be strong to gale but does not have to be. Maybe better when the front has passed/moderate to poor but can be fog on low ground as well as high	A warm sector with muggy air, fog and stratus all possible. Often much cloud but low cloud may only be Sc/if caught a long way from home it would be best to stay where you are until the weather clears?	Flying is out until the front passes. Even then the conditions need to be assessed on the spot

Cloud type or situation	Previous history	Cloud	Wind/visibility now	Expect/advice	Thermal/dynamic lift
(5) Stratocumulus (Sc) and stratocumulus lenticularis (St lent) (Photo 5)	Generally fair, maybe warm for the time of year. Sc lent only in hilly areas in stable conditions	Usually formed in an inversion and is a product of a lasting situation. Lenticularis is due to wave streaming	Usually moderate or less/good to moderate	A continuation of present weather but consult forecasts to see what may lie in store/ use ridge lift to fly as much as possible	Little thermal lift unless holes appear in the Sc sheet/ dynamic should be reliable with very little chance of a wind shift
(6) Cumulus of limited extent (Photo 7)	Fair weather	Like Photo 7 with uniform base and distance base to tops less than height of base from ground. Sometimes forms under thin layer of As or Ac in high season	Light to moderate with normal diurnal changes/good to moderate	Continuation of present weather with overnight inversions/best conditions you are likely to get	Good soaring but note how Cu may grow with the day. See next section/wind is variable but may not exceed normal gust factor
(7) Cumulus that may grown into cumulonimbus (Photo 15)	Morning cool with forecast of possible showers. Ragged Cu builds early on a gusty wind	Cumulus whose depth grows greater then height of base from the ground. Pileus caps may be seen in which case showers are very likely	Tends to be moderate by breakfast-time. Can become blustery and exceed safe gust factor/good or very good but poor if showers develop	Showers to develop during forenoon and/or afternoon, dying out with evening. Look around for orographic cap cloud/fly early and late	Can become dangerously strong with downdraughts near showers/can become overpowering by afternoon
(8) Cumulonimbus (Cb) Heavy showers and/or thunderstorms (Photos 10, 11 and 18)	Cool unstable airstream for showers but warm sultry air for storms. Morning may seem fair and tempt you into the hills. Consult f'cst and remember things go bad quickly in the hills and mountains	Like Photo 10 when showers approach. Like Photo 11 when storms approach. There may be much surrounding cloud so that heads are not easily seen	Can be moderate to fresh with showers and with some thunderstorms. For big storms wind must be light to moderate/often good before showers but poor and murky before storms	Squalls and strong up and downdraughts. Can be hail that will damage sails and wings/think before you attempt to fly	Can be some good local lift between showers but fly with an eye on the windward sky. Do not fly near the showers/ can be good locally between showers but winds shift around showers and storms. Poor ahead of bad storms

(9) Stratus (St) (Photo 8)	Warm muggy airstream. Can suddenly appear over windward slopes and over the tops. A normal accompaniment to rain from fronts	Likely to appear out of nowhere. Very difficult to decide if and when and f'cst may not help. Look at highest slopes to see if it is appearing there (Photo 9)	Usually moderate from a maritime quarter. Not if out of a large land mass like Europe but a hundred mile sea track can form it/generally poor to fog limits	To be caught out sometimes and to take care to fly close to base/if in any doubt don't!	May be some in the sun but generally poor in airstreams that are prone to St/stable wind without too many variations
(10) Coming cold front (Photo 10)	Warm sector weather	A deep mass of cloud coming in from windward horizon. Look for anvils amongst the tops or masses of Ci cloud between heads (Photo 9 background)	Often SW but will veer (usually to NW) at head of cloud mass. Squalls and heavy showers as front arrives/moderate but poor under front becoming good later	Colder air with heap clouds once front has passed. Then allow for heavy showers/if flying get down quickly and secure against wind and rain/hail. Fly again in a few hours' time?	Usually little in warm sector air. Strong downdraughts ahead of front. Strong updraughts in frontal cloud. Will become better later, maybe tomorrow/allow for wind shift to the right in planning new slope
(11) Showery airstream, possibly with airmass troughs (Photos 10 and 18)	This airstream often follows a cold front and appears behind retreating depressions	Little or none early but builds to great heights with the day. Showers do not normally distribute themselves evenly about the day but form into groups (airmass troughs) (Photo 10)	Often between W and N. Blustery near showers and troughs, often moderate or less between troughs and in rear of showers	If forecast indicates showers are expected and none appear for some time during the morning or afternoon, ask if this is not due to sinking air ahead of an airmass trough and look out for it/take precautions against deluges if hiking off into the hills early under cool blue skies – allow for later deluges	Good at first but gust factor easily exceeded later when cloud develops. A potentially dangerous airstream/usually good and often little change of wind direction except near showers
(12) Thundery sky (Photo 14)	Follows over-warm days which threaten to break down the good weather with thunderstorms in association with small local lows	Castellanus and floccus riding in, often across the surface wind direction. Often appear in the morning and after a clear hot morning/afternoon dark banks of chaotic-looking cloud bring much thunder and lightning (Photos 13 and 14)	Often not above moderate but can be odd gusts from any direction during storms. Wind may well be E and storms come up from S/often poor during morning. Better when storms have cleared the air	Thunder to occur at some altitude with much cloud-cloud (sheet) lightning. Some strikes to ground. Better tomorrow/make hay while the sun shines	Thermals may be 'explosive' in nature. Despite heat, thermals do not develop properly/expect great variation in surface wind direction and speed. There may be 45° between one phase of the wind and another

3

THE CHANGING WEATHER

Weather changes because of three main processes. Firstly, and most importantly, it changes because depressions, troughs of low pressure, anticyclones and ridges of high pressure cross the region. Secondly, it changes because things develop or conversely are rubbed out over the region. Depressions (or lows) are continually being born, growing to maturity and then dying out. Fronts can be in the process of developing (frontogenesis) or degenerating (frontolysis). You are much more likely to experience active fronts if you fly slopes facing the Atlantic than if you fly on the eastern side of a landmass. For example, many fronts which rain heavily on the backbone of mountains along the west or centre of Britain are mere shadows of their former selves by the time they reach the East Coast. Sometimes little wave depressions will ripple along a front and pass through your area, deteriorating the weather when it looked as if it was clearing. Finally, the weather scene alters because of local influences such as the sudden arrival of seabreezes (when you fly not too far from the coast) or of valley winds when you fly in the mountains.

I assume that those who read this book are not meteorologists and do not wish to become meteorologists, but you still need to be extremely conscious of weather and how it will change during the time you are flying or are preparing to fly. You cannot do without the forecasts, but no single forecast can give you the details needed for your site to make the difference between flying and not flying. Sometimes the forecast will be at an awkward time or you may have faulty batteries in your radio or for some other reason you fail to get an up-to-date forecast. So, it is important to recognise the signs of weather problems that may be creeping up, or even leaping up, on you.

Changeable weather

It is very important to recognise the processes that go on when the weather is forecast as being 'changeable'. If you look first at a weather map, you can see the up-to-date state of the weather scene from the charts that are screened on national and local TV. If you have a video recorder, then you can freeze those charts when you really want to study them by recording the telecast and then using the 'pause' facility.

What do you want to know? Firstly, what is the wind? How strong will it be over your likely site and what things will come along to change the situation for better or for worse? There is an easy way of getting a rough idea of where the wind speeds are likely to be in the 10 knot (5m/s) bracket and this is outlined in the next section. Before that, here is an introduction to some useful aspects of depression weather using an actual example.

Fig. 3.1 is a chart compiled from observations made at midday in autumn. The time of day and the time of year are important when it comes to assessing what kinds of local winds may appear to alter the wind that the isobars show. At this time of year seabreezes, for example, are hardly noticeable, except perhaps to those who are flying coastal cliffs.

It can be seen straight away that there is a low hovering out to the south-west of Britain and a big 'hole' in the isobars over France and the Low Countries. There is a curved wedge

Fig. 3.1 A weather map of Atlantic Europe for a day in October. The distance between the open arrows indicates the distance corresponding to a geostrophic wind of 10 knots when the isobars are drawn at 4 mb intervals

– a 'warm sector' – between the warm front (represented by a line with 'knobs' on) and the cold front (represented by a line with 'ice-spikes'). The air in a warm sector has to be warmer than that ahead and often a lot warmer than that behind it. So, the clouds that go with cool air – heap or, more scientifically, cumuliform clouds – can be expected to exist in the southerly airstream coming up from the Bay of Biscay.

Britain is split into three wind regions. As the closeness of the isobars indicate the strength of the wind, there is: quite a strong southerly blowing up over western and central England; a much lighter regime over Scotland and Ireland; while south-east England and East Anglia are under the sway of the light wind regime over the Continent. In other words, the south-east of England, Ireland and Scotland are flyable.

However, although the south-east is flyable now, it will not be for long. It can be seen that Low A is tracking east, because lows travel roughly parallel to the isobars in their warm sectors. Low A's isobars are pointing east and the low is on its way up the English Channel. It follows that if you want to fly somewhere in south-east England, then you'd better forgo lunch and fly now while the wind is still light enough. For as the low tracks eastwards, the strong wind corridor to the west will surely spread to you.

Wind and isobar spacing

There is a simple way of looking at the isobar spacing and getting an idea of the wind speed. The weather maps seen on TV usually have isobars drawn at intervals of 4mb (like fig. 3.1). Drawn this way, isobars that are as far apart as the width of the south of England (from the Scilly Isles to the extreme east of Kent) indicate a 10-knot wind in the space between them. Halving this spacing indicates 20 knots and halving again, 40 knots. So, at this moment south-east England and the Low Countries have the kind of light southerly which could make flying very good. Over to the west of this light area winds are a lot stronger, maybe as strong as 30-40 knots. To expand this idea for any chart and isobar spacing, see Geostrophic wind (pp. 148-51).

In this context we have an important point to remember about wind that is found from the isobar spacing. It is called the 'gradient wind' and is the wind that is free of the earth's friction. It blows faster than the surface wind and it will represent the wind around 2000ft up. The increase in the wind strength between the ground and a few thousand feet aloft is called the 'wind gradient' and this must not be confused with the 'gradient wind'. More will be found about wind gradient in chapter 6.

Quasi-stationary lows and fronts

So, just looking at the weather map tells us at once that at this moment there are flying conditions for hang gliders and paragliders over the landmasses surrounding the southern North Sea and over most of France. Balloonists may not have enough time to get airborne in England but could well do so over France.

Low A is a travelling depression and will carry its weather with it, but Low B near the Shetlands is hardly going to move anywhere. The correct term for this lack of definite motion is 'quasi-stationary'. One of these relatively fixed depression areas can be identified by the way the isobars enclose the low pressure area. It is an elongated region laced by a front. This front that snakes through the area is sometimes a warm one and sometimes a cold one. It all depends on which way it wriggles at any one time. The air around Low A has to be colder than the air in its warm sector, but there can be even colder air around and that really cold air is to the north-west of the quasi-stationary front.

The rule for naming fronts is:

the air behind the front gives its name to the front.

As the warmest air is in the warm sector over Biscay, there is a warm front from Low A into central Spain and, as the air off the west coast of Spain is colder, a cold front loops down through Finisterre. That is a classic phenomenon and is found in all met. text books. The quasi-stationary front through Low B, however, is not moving anywhere very much. Sometimes it moves towards the very cold air as a warm front and sometimes away from it as a cold front. In practice that means the zone surrounding such fronts is one where flying conditions will be abysmal and you might as well forget it.

Travelling Low A

The weather over south-east England can be guessed, because of the way warm fronts behave and the clouds they produce. You may well not have any access to a weather map on site, but you should have looked at one either on the breakfast TV or the night before.

With the aid of their massive computers, the professional met. people can get to-morrow's chart right when it comes to wind speed and direction, but they may not get the weather exactly right because the computer cannot tell them that – it just forecasts isobars. Thus you have to keep an eye on your own patch of sky to see what is happening.

Let's assume that as it has been a sunny morning with light wind, you have gone to a Downland venue to try your luck and you have had some quite good flying during the forenoon (0800–1200 LST; 'early morning' is any time after the sun is up). But what about the afternoon? If you don't note the signs in the sky, you could, quite suddenly, find the afternoon deteriorates badly. The wind and turbulence could soon increase and perhaps make it impossible for you to return to your launch site. What should you look for? The answers are to be found in the structure of warm fronts.

Facts about warm fronts

Warm fronts are surfaces of separation between relatively warm air lying a wedge over colder air below (see fig. 3.2). The warm air is moist and is lifted along the frontal surface so

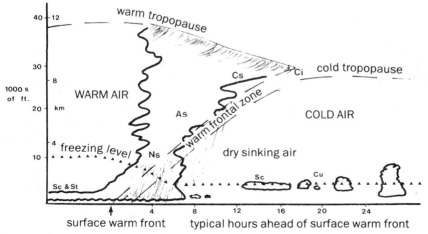

Fig. 3.2 Cross-section through an ana warm front, showing typical clouds and weather. Note the change in the freezing level

that it condenses out as cloud. This cloud usually gets thick enough to rain or snow. The characteristic skyscapes that precede the precipitation are a sign of deterioration. As it is normal for the wind to increase and shift direction as well, noting these skyscapes can have a great bearing on planning your flying in the next few hours (see photographs 1 and 2).

The typical weather well ahead of a coming warm front is ideal for flying. It will normally be slightly unstable and so there will be limited thermal lift. The visibility will usually be very good and sometimes exceptional, so you will have a marvellous view from your aerial platform. Such extreme visibility has been recognised for a long time as heralding poor weather. A bit of seafaring lore says:

'When the Lizard is clear, rain is near!'

which means that the 186 feet high most southerly promontory in Britain stands out crystal clear in the air that exists ahead of a coming warm front.

Air gets full of obscuring particles when it travels over industrial areas and other conurbations, but air that sinks from above is free of such particulates. It is because the air below the warm frontal surface sinks that visibility is so good there. This sinking air also destroys cloud so that the vault below the first whispy clouds of the coming warm front often becomes quite free of cloud. Cumulus cloud that has grown in the ridge of high pressure that precedes a coming depression will begin to evaporate away as the warm front extends its influence over the site, and this signifies diminishing lift. Here are the major things to look for.

Signs of a coming warm front

Whisps of cirrus (Ci) cloud that invade the high troposphere, together with dense and persistent vapour trails, are the first signs of a coming warm front or occlusion (see photograph 1). Cumulus that begins to flatten and maybe spread out eventually to disappear altogether is also an important sign. Expect a wind shift from a typical W or NW direction back towards S as time progresses, and the previously slightly unstable air to become very much more stable so that it becomes progressively more difficult to remain airborne.

Ahead of an active warm front (called an 'ana' warm front) the cirrus should increase in amount with time and gradually change into another form – cirrostratus (Cs) (see fig. 3.2 and photograph 2). This is easy to recognise, because a large ring halo develops about the sun. When Cs progressively replaces Ci then, without any other forecast, you can be much surer that bad weather is on the way.

You can confirm it when the darker cloud layers of altostratus (As) gather and begin to blot out the sun (see photograph 3). The previous two cloud types (Ci and Cs) were so high in the atmosphere that they were composed wholly of ice crystals. For this reason they were also entirely white. However, lower cloud layers are composed of water droplets and these can appear dark and shadowed. The typical description of the sun being lost behind thickening layers of ground glass is very apt when As invades the sky. Usually the wind will have increased somewhat by now, but the way the wind speed alters as lows approach can be very variable. It is almost universally known that when a low tracks to the north of you the wind direction backs into the southern quadrants. From fig. 3.1 it is also obvious that winds are often going to be southerly ahead of lows that will later track south of you, as Low A is set to do as far as flying in Britain is concerned.

As the altostratus gathers and thickens, turbulence will be induced in the increasing wind strength, but thermals will have long since ceased to exist. One of the first bits of weather forecasting I ever learned was from my mother who foretold bad weather when (a) the smoke from the chimney blew down, and (b) the sash windows began 'to jigget'. The first of these *ad hoc* rules indicates sinking as opposed to rising currents and the second shows the jumble of gusts and lulls in the turbulent eddies that form as the wind gathers in strength. Both spell the end of any thoughts of flying until the weather improves.

The normal sequence of events is for the cloud to thicken until it rains, when the rain cloud has become nimbostratus (Ns) and may well be solid to 20,000 feet or more while below it a form of stratus called pannus (St pan) develops and brings the cloudbase down to possibly as little as 1000 feet (see photograph 4). The rain belt can be more or less continuous for some hours before the warm front passes at the surface. Then the sky lightens and the rain ceases; there can be a temporary break before more low cloud develops while the temperature and humidity both rise. The 'sensation' description of temperature and humidity is 'muggy' in most warm sectors and the characteristic clouds are thick stratocumulus (Sc) (see photograph 9) and/or stratus (St) (see photograph 8) as well as layers of altocumulus (Ac) (see photograph 12) and some cirrus. On the slopes facing the wind – which is characteristically SW – the upslope effect can occasionally have it raining or drizzling continuously for most of the time the warm sector takes to pass.

Facts about cold fronts

Flying is out until more trouble has passed. That trouble is the cold front. Cold fronts are normally more active than warm fronts. At their head there is usually a line of very unstable air lifted mechanically by the cold air pushing vigorously in under the warm air (see fig. 3.3). The updraught speed at their leading edge may be about 10 knots (5 m/s) and the

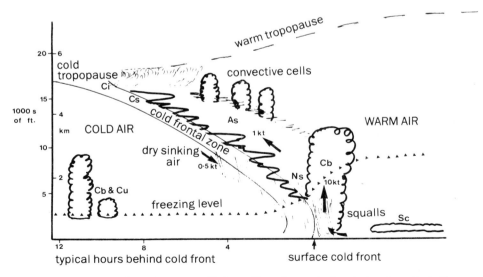

Fig. 3.3 Cross-section through an ana cold front. Note the speed of typical updraughts in the cumulonimbus clouds at the head of the front. The high level convective cells account for local increases in the intensity of rain (or snow) fall

result is heavy showers and squalls induced by the heavy rain or hail. There may be some thunder also. Ahead of and behind this relatively narrow but violent band of convective weather there is sinking air. The sinking air ahead often breaks what has been up to then a very cloudy sky, and enables the towering nimbostratus and cumulonimbus of the front to be seen approaching (see photograph 9). However, it may not always do so. The sinking air behind the early bluster is accompanied by much lighter and fairly continuous rain that is occasionally interspersed by heavier bursts from high altitude convective cells. This rain clears in about half the time it took the warm front rain to clear, leaving Ci bands to trail along the often clear-cut back edge of the retreating frontal cloud (see photograph 22).

There is almost always a slot of clear sky behind a cold front. This opens up an advancing sheet of sunshine which heats the ground and, after a while, allows thermals to develop. There is plenty of moisture on the ground following the frontal rain and so the Cu that develops may well be extensive. The cold air also deepens and very often Cb clouds develop, leading to heavy showers. Do not be fooled into thinking that the weather has cleared when the front passes and the sun shines. You may just get airborne when the showers start to develop (see photograph 10).

Older fronts

The passage of the active (ana) fronts of a youthful depression has now been described, but many, maybe most, fronts of eastern Britain and continental Europe are not ana but kata fronts (see fig. 3.4). The air over kata fronts is only rising in a few places. Air over the higher reaches of the fronts is sinking and eroding high- and medium-level clouds. This process

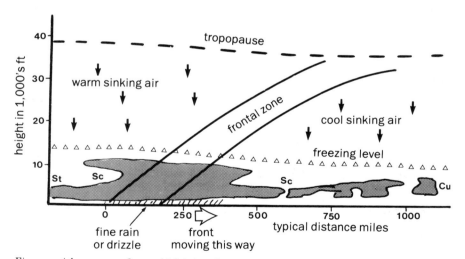

Fig. 3.4 A kata warm front which is in a late stage of decay. Many fronts are in some other stage between this and a pure ana front

leads to fronts that may only possess relatively thin cloud masses and so will not produce precipitation of the intensity of ana fronts. Kata cold fronts (see fig. 3.5), for example, may have only light showers at their head and even lighter ones behind. The fate of most

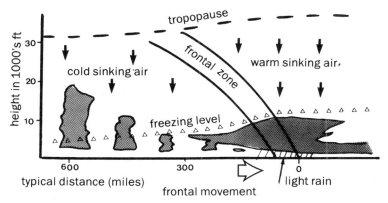

Fig. 3.5 A kata cold front. While the freezing level changes across the front, surface changes may be much less well-marked

depressions is to be eaten away from the top by subsiding and warming airmasses from high up. Subsiding air is the accompaniment to rising pressure and to the building of ridges of high pressure and anticyclones.

Anticyclones and ridges

Between the members of a family of depressions there will be ridges of high pressure (see fig. 3.6). Here the isobars will curve in the opposite sense to the way they encircle depressions or bend round troughs of low pressure. When a run of lows comes to an end it is a

Fig. 3.6 Diagram showing how the surface winds (open arrows) blow across the isobars at an angle out of high into low, and also what the pressure features, ridge, trough and col look like on the weather map

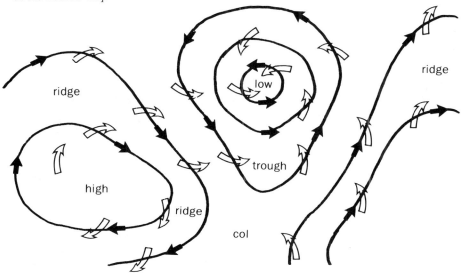

large quasi-stationary high that usually takes over. Such anticyclones are called 'blocking' highs, because they block the normal run of lows around the temperate latitudes of either hemisphere. The lows still run from west to east under the impetus of the upper winds, but those winds are deflected north and south of the blocking high. This leads to unseasonal weather in, say, Spain and parts of the Mediterranean when a blocking high has brought weeks of settled weather to Atlantic Europe's shores. Otherwise, smaller anticyclones exist between the lows and travel with them from west to east. Blocking highs may in some cases travel 'retrograde' from east to west, but this is a fairly rare occurrence just as lows that travel against the normal direction are equally rare. Normally, the lows and highs travel eastwards round the temperate latitudes in one vast merry-go-round of the hemisphere.

All high pressure regions will have air over them that is sinking from very high up. This sinking air has to flow out sideways, but at the same time it also has to follow the isobars at about 2000 feet – a level which is sufficiently high up to be free of surface friction. It is near the surface that the roughness of the ground allows the air to blow out of high pressure regions at an angle which may be 30 degrees on average, but it can be considerably larger and somewhat smaller sometimes (see chapter 6). Because of this, air sinks and blows out of highs and ridges and into lows (see fig. 3.6) where it can rise again.

Just as rising air cools (and condenses its water vapour into cloud and precipitation), so sinking air warms up and evaporates the water droplets of clouds. Thus the upper air over high pressure regions is normally clear of clouds, but that does not mean that the air nearer the ground is clear. On the contrary, the subsiding air forms a temperature inversion and often thick Sc cloud forms in this inversion and may produce a total cover. This is particularly likely in the winter half of the year when the sun has less power to 'burn off' the cloud sheet. In summer the subsidence inversion is the cause of excessively hot days with explosive but limited convection, leading to much frustration and indeed some danger for air riders. The day when it is 90°F (32°C) in the shade and there is a totally blue sky may not be a good day for flying. In its attempts to escape upwards the over-stressed air can behave violently and in so doing unbalance a hang glider or partially collapse a parafoil. You might expect a lot of lift on such hot summer days, but the air will often be sluggish and, at the same time, treacherous.

More benign inversions in more normal highs and ridges will limit the convection to, say, 4000–5000 feet, but will still provide wonderful flying weather. By the very nature of the sport most flying will be done under anticyclone conditions, with gentle winds and fair weather cumulus dotting the sky. Such days dawn cool and cloud-free. If a cloud-free early morning is very hot, beware of 'blue' thermals generated suddenly and unpredictably.

Only the way that travelling lows and highs can alter the weather have been covered here. More information about such phenomena as airmass troughs (which look like cold fronts, but are not), weak fronts and occlusions, wave depressions, etc. is provided in Part 2.

TABLE 3.1 CHECK ON FRONTAL WEATHER

Use this table to prompt questions on the conditions when active (ana) warm fronts are forecast. The forecast will indicate that rain and wind will spread across the area — usually from the west. The first column suggests where you are in the weather sequence from the look of the sky. You may follow it from the good weather ahead (1) right through to when conditions become unflyable or you may insert at say (2) or (3).

Sky now	Sky was	You are	Air state now	Likely to become	Wind/convection/turbulence		Visibility	Remarks
					Now	*Later*		
(1) Cu under Ci. Sunny periods	No Ci	In last of ridge before deterioration	Normal or diminishing convection	Stable or sinking	From light to 10–15kt. Often NW–N/normal gust/lull pattern/low level	Freshening/gust/lull pattern decreasing/increasing	Very good or exceptional	This is where you may well come in as this has been good flying weather
(2) Increasing Ci, decreasing Cu or Cu spreading into Sc, often lenticular	Increasing Ci with eroding Cu	In first of coming low's circulation	Limited, unpredictable convection. Stabilising	Stable or sinking air	Increasing and backing towards S/no structured gust/lull pattern/increasing	Further increasing and backing/forget any structure in gusts and lulls/increasing	Very good or exceptional	High cloud now invading sky with a vengeance. If wind is not increasing, why not? Still upslope (mechanical) lift
(3) Mainly Cs with some Ci. Normally little lower cloud	Ci, no Cu	Some hours into circulation of low	Little or no thermal lift	No thermal lift	As above	As above	Good	Look for halos about the sun. Maybe sun-dogs in afternoon or evening

Sky now	Sky was	You are	Air state now	Likely to become	Wind/convection/turbulence		Visibility	Remarks
					Now	Later		
(4) Gathering As or wholly As	Cs	A few hours from rain	Many descending currents	No thermal lift	Worse	Southerly should be established, maybe increasing/only turbulent eddies	Decreasing but not bad	Look for sun being lost and after some time expect pannus and rain
(5) Total cover of Ns and low pannus	As	In the rain belt	Downdraughts dangerous for flying. Plus extra weight of rain	Similar	Increase in rain/only turbulent eddies	Expect rain to stop in a matter of hours	Moderate maybe poor	Nothing to do but wait for a final clearance
(6) Clearance appears with fracto stratus below cloud base	Ns	At point of warm front clearance	Air usually sinks behind frontal cloud	Similar	Wind shifts clockwise, may change speed up or down/ maybe limited convection if sky really clears	New direction is often SW and remains that way/usually cloudy so no convection/ turbulent eddies if wind strong	Temporary improvement often followed by decrease later. Can be fog, mist or drizzle	Some warm fronts clear to hazy sunshine and warmth. Most lead to lots of cloud and a muggy feel to the air

Once you recognise that you are in the warm sector of a depression the weather you have is the weather you will keep very often. Occasionally the pressure will rise behind a warm front and push any coming cold air away. Then you can have several days of warm humid weather. Convection is inhibited in such warm airstreams and there may be thunder once the wind eases. More normally orographic rain occurs over slopes facing the wind with hill fog and drizzle on coasts. The next major event – necessary for good flying weather to return – is the passage of a cold front.

4
THE SHIFTING WIND

The wind changes direction and speed on four scales.

(1) Long-period shifts occupying times involving a day or more. These are brought about by changes in the local pressure pattern as lows and highs move through the area.

(2) Meso-scale shifts taking a matter of hours to accomplish. These can be due to pressure pattern changes, but also to complex frontal systems. Fronts may look like lines on the weather map, but many fronts take hours to pass and after they have finally cleared the new wind direction will have come about through several minor shifts of direction. Changes due to local winds, such as mountain and valley winds and in some instances land and seabreezes, may take hours to change from one phase to another. Shifts due to thunderstorms may also fall in this category.

(3) Mini-scale shifts occupying a matter of minutes which may appear when sharp cold fronts or seabreeze fronts pass. This is also the scale of the shift pattern on heap cloud days when gusts and lulls chase one another across the countryside.

(4) Micro-scale shifts are those which pass in seconds and are due to the wind blowing over, round and through objects. This is the scale of mechanical turbulence.

Long-period shifts

These are important to paraglider and hang glider pilots, because they are usually limited in their choice of slopes from which to fly. These slopes may not cover as wide a span of the compass as they might like and so getting the right wind direction governs whether they can fly or not. Therefore, a long-period shift divined from a TV or radio forecast, or from personal observations, may make it possible to fly later, or induce you to fly now. It may make you abandon any idea of flying as you realise that the wind, which is at present blowing nicely onto your chosen slope, will have shifted off it by the time you get there. Also, such shifts go with definite weather patterns which can govern your capacity to fly. The long-period backing shifts that occur ahead of deteriorating weather are a case in point. Any thermal lift there may be now will soon disappear under gathering cloud layers. Conversely, the wind that slowly veers into the NW or N behind a retreating low can bring a convective airstream and make for some excellent flying tomorrow, if not today.

When a depression centre tracks across the country the chances of that centre passing to the north of you are great when you fly in England and similar latitudes of Europe. However, this is not always the case. Lows that come further south prefer tracking through the English Channel when they come in from the South-west Approaches. They may track into France or turn north-eastwards into the Low Countries. There is no 'no-go area' for depressions.

Because the wind shifts are so complex when a low centre tracks close to your site, they are described (particularly in the shipping forecasts) as 'cyclonic'. This means that you have to make up your own mind as to what will happen to the wind and that depends on where the centre goes (see fig. 4.1). If it tracks to the north of you (A), the winds will shift

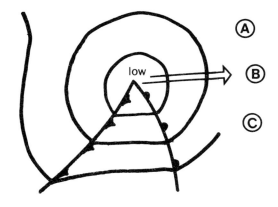

Fig. 4.1 To illustrate cyclonic changes in wind direction when a low traverses the area

differently from when it tracks south (C) and differently again when you lie under its path (B). The only thing to do is to explain what has to happen to the wind direction, etc. in these three cases, and then you can make up your own mind with the help of table 4.1 and the more extensive tables at the end of the chapter.

TABLE 4.1 TYPICAL CYCLONIC WIND AND WEATHER CHANGES (Fig 4.1)

Position with respect to low centre	(A)	(B)	(C)
Wind at first	E to SE and may be anything from light to fresh	Between S and E, strength as (A)	S to SE, possibly fresh to strong
Weather at first	Clouding over if not already overcast. Visibility usually good, occasionally poor	Cloudy or overcast. Some rain possible. Visibility normally good	Cloud and rain increasing as is normal with a warm front or occlusion approaching
Wind later	Backing E to NE and may fall lighter	Light variable and possibly calm for a time in the eye of the low. Very near centre – expect odd wind directions	Veering SW to S
Weather later	Periods of rain or drizzle. Misty but rarely foggy	Often very low cloud with fairly continuous rain or drizzle	Clearance to warm sector kind of weather. Risk of fog
Wind finally	Backing W to NW and picking up in speed	Picking up from a westerly point. Possibly increasing strong or even gale	Veering W to NW with passage of a cold front. Expect squalls
Weather finally	Rain, drizzle and low cloud slow to clear. Visibility may remain poor for a considerable time	Slow clearance of low cloud and rain. Eventually heap cloud airstream. Troughs swinging round centre deteriorate the weather very often	Clearance to clearer cooler airstream – typically mP airstream. End of any fog risk

When a succession of lows cross the country, there are usually ridges of high pressure between them (see fig. 4.2). The wind behind a retreating low (like Low (A)) is likely to be NW or W and, as the ridge advances, any showers there may have been will die out (position (A)) to be replaced by fair weather cumulus. Now for a while you have good flying weather, but you have to make the most of it, because many ridges do not last for more than a day or so.

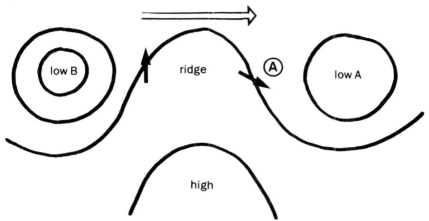

Fig. 4.2 Between travelling lows there are travelling ridges in which the weather temporarily improves. Amongst the signs of the next low a wind which backs towards south is very important

As the axis of the ridge passes, the wind will back, but it often goes down in speed and then, as the ridge moves eastwards, the wind will back further to come from SW and eventually S. There should be signs of the next low (Low B) in the sky by now (see section 3 of tables 1A and 1B).

Occasionally highs build and remain over one locality for' days, weeks or, in some exceptional cases, months. These quasi-stationary highs will bring more or less fair weather for days on end, but it is very rare for two succeeding days to be exactly the same in their wind regimes or state of stability. On the edges of the good weather systems the weather will be unseasonal and winds can be very strong even though the skies may be cloudless (see Blocking highs).

Meso-scale shifts

These are of the kind that make a favourite slope unflyable in the course of a day's flying. A warm day may have little in the way of thermal lift but may have good dynamic lift which suddenly goes bad when a cold front moves through. That certainly puts the lid on flying until it has passed, but it can be worth waiting through the rain for the unstable air in the rear. However, the wind in the colder air behind the front will most often be coming from a direction to the right of that you had before the front, which could take it right off your slope. Frontal shifts can be greater than a right angle and you might spend the intervening period of poor weather assessing if there is anywhere from which to fly when it is all over.

Even kata fronts, which have had most of the fire taken out of them and which can only produce light rain and drizzle, can produce sizeable shifts. However, in this case the shift often takes place slowly over a period measured in hours (see chapter 3).

Other shifts in this bracket are those produced by seabreezes (see chapter 9). It is only in the early morning that pilots will usually experience the effects of nocturnal winds. The night wind will continue to blow through into the early forenoon when it comes off inland mountains and you are not too many miles from the main coastline. As night winds need clear skies to develop fully, so they will often blow themselves out under morning sunshine, which is followed by calm before an opposing seabreeze develops. The night wind in mountainous districts is called a 'mountain wind' and its opposite number is the 'valley wind' which blows by day and is at its best in the afternoon and early evening (see chapter 10).

There are thunderstorms and thunderstorms. Some are just isolated Cb clouds which give a few claps of thunder and are gone, while others are massive affairs which go on for hours and are responsible for death and destruction. You will find more information about the different kinds of storms in chapter 11, but here it should be noted that storms take over the local wind scene, creating their own winds which can be highly dangerous to gliders not only in the air but also on the ground. The wind before a big storm will very often be a stable, gentle one, but it is a wind of the storm's own making and therefore due to be replaced by a savage squall as the arch-cloud of the storm rears overhead. The wind behind such storm areas can be entirely different from that which existed before. The same may go for big showers when they are formed in groups. Such groups occur in maritime Polar (mP) airmasses and are called airmass troughs. However, it is unlikely that they will produce as large a wind shift as sometimes occurs with thunderstorms.

Mini-scale shifts

These will often be experienced by glider pilots, as they are a natural accompaniment to flying days with limited convection. The gust and lull patterns that accompany days with ranks of Cu across the sky tend to have a repeat period of several minutes (why this should be so is covered in chapter 6). Gusts are of particular importance to paraglider pilots who need to fly within the limits of the normally accepted gust factor (see page 153).

Gliders should not be flying when the sharp shifts due to ana warm and cold fronts occur, but you should be aware of these shifts so that their effects can be allowed for. Seabreeze fronts are another matter, because the winds on either side of them are not going to be strong and they can provide certain lift. Anyway, they appear on fair days when thermal lift is at its best, so the fact that the wind direction may shift through as much as 180° in a minute or less is not such a hazard as it might otherwise be. It will change a slope that looks into the wind into one which has to be abandoned, but seabreeze fronts will rarely be dangerous.

Micro-scale shifts

Micro-scale shifts present a problem in that they are rapid and short-lived, and only take seconds to pass. They can cover quite a wide spectrum of directions and speeds, and their physical size will increase with the wind speed, but their frequency will remain much the same. They constitute what is called 'mechanical turbulence', and are due to collisions with objects and over-turnings in the air as it blows over land (less over the sea). When mechanical turbulence is accompanied by limited convection, as occurs on most flying days, it becomes built onto the back of the thermally-induced mini-scale shift pattern and often tends to mask the latter, more important, wind shifts.

Factors that may change the wind

For ease of reference and assessment the above, and other, facts have been put into table form. Table 4.2 gives suggestions as to what may happen to change the wind at inland hill sites. Table 4.3 is similar, but is for those sites which could be subject to seabreezes and so may experience seabreeze frontal effects. Tables A are for the morning period and Tables B for the afternoon and evening.

TABLE 4.2A THINGS THAT MAY CHANGE THE WIND   Inland Hill Sites   Winds for Morning Flying

Use these pages to suggest what might happen to the wind at these sites and at this time of day. If your site should be within the throw of the seabreezes then consult (3A) and (3B). Not every circumstance can be covered but maybe the categories in column one will make you aware of why the wind might change.

Could change because of	Possible Result	Possible reasons	Action or comments
(1) Increase in local pressure gradient (i.e. isobars tighten)	(1) (2) Too strong to fly. Increase in turbulence into the afternoon	(1) Encroaching low or trough	(1) (2) Limit your flying sessions to before wind increases
(2) Normal increase with the day	(2) Can suddenly pick up some time after breakfast	(2) Breaking of overnight inversion	(2) If calm or light at breakfast-time allow for wind to suddenly pick up during the morning
(3) Direction of isobars shifting as low or trough comes in	Winds back ahead of coming lows and troughs. Winds usually increase (See (1))	(a) A depression is routed to pass to the north of your site	(a) Winds often go from westerly to southerly points, so what will that mean for the slope you are flying?
		(b) A depression is routed to pass south of your site	(b) Winds often go from easterly to northerly points. So what will it do later?
(4) Fronts passing	Sudden (or fairly sudden) veer as worst weather passes	A sudden sharp veer is often due to a cold front. Warm fronts and occlusions may not be so marked	Strong ana fronts will preclude flying as precipitation and strong thermal turbulence may be involved. Think what to do when the front has passed and the wind you have now has maybe shifted clockwise $90°$ or more
(5) Higher degree of instability	Growth of big Cu or Cb with strong up and downdraughts. Strong gusts near showers. Gusts bring strong wind into previously sheltered parts	Continued sunshine heats ground and leads to greater vertical ascent of air. Or maybe a more unstable airmass comes along (behind a cold front or occlusion)	Watch growth of morning Cu and look for their depth increasing with time. You may be able to fly again later when this front or trough has passed. Canopies and sails need protection against rain and especially hail
(6) Change in speed (up or down) or direction bringing wind from a valley or hill (mountain) side not previously affecting your site	New direction and/or speed can induce new patterns into lift bands	Any of the above categories	When you fly a site look around for the possibilities. What would happen if the wind suddenly shifted left or right of its present direction?

Could change because of	Possible Result	Possible reasons	Action or comments
(7) An anabatic wind setting in	A breeze develops towards higher slopes (or peaks) in sunlight	Sunshine on a hill or mountain side will lead to an up-slope wind. Air from your site may have to flow to fill the partial vacuum	Can provide a wind towards higher ground when none was expected or reinforce an already up-slope wind
(8) A valley wind setting in	Towards the end of a quiet morning a wind develops towards a local valley looking into mountains	Anabatics up slopes higher up the valley draw air along valley floor	In some mountain locations this is a reliable wind in quiet weather. Ask the locals
(9) A seabreeze front arriving	A light breeze develops from direction of main sea coast after a period of calm. See (4.3A)(4.3B)	Seabreeze sets in against a wind which has blown lightly towards main sea coast	If wind falters by end of morning (when it should be increasing) suspect a seabreeze, maybe aided by (7) or (8). The wind must be light before the breeze. A calm sunny morning can bring this breeze up to thirty miles inland. (Also think of lake winds when applicable)
(10) Thunderstorms or heavy showers over hill or mountain slopes inland	Sudden arrival of dangerous cold squally winds from higher ground	Downdraught 'gales' due to heavy rain and/or hail up-slope from your site. Winds may arrive some time after storms that had scarcely been seen or heard	This is a highly dangerous situation and should be considered whenever the forecast goes for storms and you fly a site with a backing of mountains. Sailplane pilots have been killed by such winds

TABLE 4.2B THINGS THAT MAY CHANGE THE WIND   Inland Hill Sites   Winds for Afternoon and Evening Flying

The afternoon is dominated by the strongest winds of the day which will mute with onset of evening. These changes follow the normal pattern unless the local pressure pattern is changing rapidly or local wind influences take over.

Could change because of	Possible results	Possible reasons	Action or comments
(1) Increase in local pressure gradient (isobars tighten)	Normal fall in wind speed in late afternoon does not occur. Wind stays up or even increases	Encroaching low or trough	Expect wind to increase and back into the evening and night

Could change because of	Possible results	Possible reasons	Action or comments
(2) Normal diurnal variation	Wind increases into middle of afternoon then decreases. Turbulence more or less suddenly decreases late afternoon. Evening may tend towards laminar flow	Sunshine raises air temperature until about 2-3 p.m. LST. Then surface temperature decreases and inversion begins to form. Thermals weaken and become limited	If wind too strong and gusty in the middle of the afternoon, then could get good conditions late afternoon or evening
(3) Direction of isobars shifting as low or trough comes in	Winds back ahead of coming lows and troughs. Could become quite strong with strong turbulence	(a) Depression is routed to pass to north of your site (b) Depression is routed to pass south of your site	(a) Winds often go from westerly to southerly points, so what will that mean for the slope you are flying? (b) Winds often go from easterly to northerly points. So what will that mean for tomorrow?
(4) Fronts passing	See same section in (4.2A)		
(5) Higher degree of instability	Afternoon is the most likely time for showers to break out, dying out with evening. See same section (4.2A)	May be normal diurnal effect or some change of airmass (a front has passed)	Watch the growth of the highest Cu tops. Look for deep solid clouds which develop cauliflower-like tops. A certain sign of strong upward development is pileus skeins on the sides of the growing clouds
(6) Change in speed (up or down) or direction bringing wind from a valley or hill (mountain) side not previously affecting your site	See same section (4.2A)		
(7) A katabatic wind setting in	A breeze comes down from higher slopes that were sunlit but are now in shadow	Loss of sun from hill or mountain sides will, after a time, result in cold air draining off the sides	Can stem a previously up-slope wind leading to calm – most prevalent in evening and early night
(8) A valley wind setting in	Valley wind blows from early afternoon and strengthens into the evening	Anabatics over many hill or mountain sides need to be fed by a wind along the valley floor	In some mountain locations this is a reliable wind in quiet weather. Find out about this and other local winds by asking the locals
(9) A seabreeze front arriving	A calming of the previously light wind which was blowing towards a	Sun and Cu during the morning have drawn in the breeze against	If wind falters during mid-afternoon when it should be at its strongest suspect that a seabreeze front is

main sea coast, followed by a breeze from that direction	the opposing wind. If thirty miles inland do not expect breeze before late afternoon or the evening	imminent. The further from the coast, the later the breeze will arrive. It may not even get to you despite getting to places closer to the coast. It may also stop over you and produce a long period of calm
(10) Thunderstorms or heavy showers over hill or mountain slopes inland	Sudden arrival of dangerous cold squally winds from direction of Massif	Downdraught 'gales'. See same section (4.2A)	Much more likely in late afternoon or during the evening than in the morning. If any signs appear, get down and secure your gear

TABLE 4.3A THINGS THAT MAY CHANGE THE WIND Coastal sites within normal throw of seabreezes (coastline to 20 miles)   Morning Flying Winds

The conditions of sunshine, light winds and limited instability which are also good for gliding are also good for seabreezes. So the glider pilot will meet fronts etc. quite often. For seabreeze fronts morning wind must be from some point opposed to the seabreeze direction. If wind already blowing from the coast, seabreeze effect will enhance it and maybe make it more turbulent. S-B = seabreeze

Could change because of	Possible results	Possible reasons	Action or comments
(1) Early onset of S-B at coastal cliff sites; later onset progressively further inland	Wind shifts to on-shore direction after a period of calm. Shift may be sudden and up to 180°	Breeze has to overcome and push back the opposing wind so there has to be a front between, where air is rising strongly	Except when morning starts calm, seabreeze fronts cannot penetrate too far inland during the forenoon. An average speed of advance is 4 knots (less near the coast, more further inland). Even if breeze comes ashore as early as 9 a.m. it can only be 10-12 miles inland by midday
(2) An anabatic wind setting in	At coastal cliff sites in early sun, anabatic drift can draw in an early seabreeze. Anabatics over slopes of coastal hills can do the same	Sun on slopes that see it early will induce up-slope breezes. Lowlands may still be shadowed or not so rapidly heated	These can be very stable beginners' winds, but you will have to start very early to catch them. Mornings need to be calm or nearly so
(3) Increase in local pressure gradient (isobars tighten)	If seabreeze has already set in, it could be ousted by strengthening gradient	Encroaching low pressure area or a high developing	Expect some unreliable winds with big and often chaotic wind shifts as developing gradient wind fights the established breeze. Otherwise see (4.2A) or (4.2B) Section (1)

Could change because of	Possible results	Possible reasons	Action or comments
(4) Decrease in local pressure gradient (isobars slacken)	If wind at breakfast-time is too strong for S–B but is decreasing, S–B could set in late morning	Pressure rising over the site	If forecast has gone for wind decreasing during the morning, and other conditions are in favour, you could get an unexpected on-shore wind shift. If wind too strong for flying now, it could be OK by afternoon
(5) Higher degree of instability	On unstable days seabreezes may set in before the big Cu of Cb have a chance to develop. Then S–B can be violently ousted by squalls from showers. Otherwise a new unstable airmass can help induce a seabreeze when one was not expected	Air above inversion can be unstable to great heights and so when it breaks large-scale convection can ensue. Or a front could introduce a new airmass	Look out if big shower clouds threaten land before trouble occurs. Most likely towards lunch-time and after. Winds can swing in and out with periods of calm interspersed with violent gusts. Can be a thundery tendency with altocumulus floccus and castellanus around during a warm morning
(6) Change of speed (up or down) or direction bringing wind from a valley or hill (mountain) side not previously directing the wind over your site	Seabreeze onset can shift speed and direction from a slope facing inland with dynamic lift to opposite direction, completely altering the lift band pattern	Seabreeze front moves over the site, introducing a large shift of direction	Note conditions for seabreeze setting in at your site and look for calming effects and cloud-line of approaching front. Maybe not before afternoon if more than 10 miles inland
(7) A valley wind setting in	In high coastal areas a valley wind can also pull in seabreeze and provide a fresh wind – maybe too fresh	Late morning sunshine on high slopes inland will induce the valley wind	The valley wind is for the afternoon hours and as coastal valleys look away from the sea so valley wind plus seabreeze plus maybe a constriction effect of a narrowing valley can produce fresh to strong winds in an otherwise light wind regime
(8) Onset of falling winds in high coastal areas	Arrival (sometimes sudden) of strong (even gale) force winds from inland mountains, especially if snow-covered	Cold mountain tops aided by gradient wind bring super katabatics whistling down through the coastal valleys	These are winds like the Mistral of the Gulf of Lions and the Bora of the Adriatic. Opposing seabreeze forces lead to least wind in middle of day and most in early forenoon and during the evening. Great care needed flying such terrain

TABLE 4.3B THINGS THAT MAY CHANGE THE WIND (2B)
Coastal sites within normal throw of seabreezes (Coastline to 20 miles) Afternoon Flying Winds

See notes at head of 4.3A. In the afternoon there is much greater chance of seabreezes invading inland areas, and pilots should look out for them.

Could change because of	Possible results	Possible reasons	Action or comments
(1) Coastal sites close to the sea. (a) Late onset of a S-B against what was a 10-15kt wind from a landward point (b) Re-establishment of land wind when S-B has blown for much of the day	(a) More or less sudden shift to sea direction but may not last long. Note any calming effects on previously quite noticeable wind speed (b) Often a calming of S-B towards evening followed by reversal	(a) Land wind of 10 or more knots is on the edge of the ability of strongest seabreeze forces to reverse. So takes to middle of afternoon to achieve any effect, then only near coast (b) The pent-up land wind is only waiting to push the breeze back into the sea. Gradient wind may have strengthened	Late seabreezes are often erratic in onset and duration. They could make cliff flying hazardous as wind swings violently about (b) The seabreeze front will still be visible on many occasions but only as a ghost of its former self. However, the cloud-line will look odd with its 'cloud curtains' hanging below it. Expect wind to reverse near to the cloud-line
(2) Coastal sites inland from main sea coast. (a) Late S-B onset (not usually above 10 miles inland) (b) Re-establishment of land wind	(a) As (1a) above but the further inland, the later any breeze will be and the less likely. Often all that happens is a fall in land wind speed (b) As (1b) above	(a) As (1a) above and only strongest S-B forces can create breeze when land wind has kept the breeze at bay so long (b) As (1b) above but gradient need not have strengthened when near the maximum throw of the S-B	(a) As (1a) above (b) As (1b) above
(3) Increase in local pressure gradient (all sites)	As normal maximum speed in mid-afternoon, so increase in gradient (if in same direction) can make it too strong to fly	Often due to a low or trough approaching, so look for high cloud build-up	Take note of forecast of wind increase. Do not confuse with normal diurnal increase in wind speed. If wind does not fall with evening allow for strengthening and backing
(4) Decrease in local pressure gradient (all sites)	Unexpected S-B can appear when morning land wind was too strong for S-B	Slackening wind speed opposing the S-B forces often go with developing fair weather so there can be late shift of wind to S-B	Note forecast of possible wind decrease with the day but do not confuse with normal drop in wind speed with evening

Could change because of	Possible results	Possible reasons	Action or comments
(5) Change of speed (up or down) or direction bringing wind from a valley or hill-side not previously directing the wind over your site	In a constricting valley looking up from the sea the breeze could well become quite strong – much stronger than the land wind	Valleys narrow inland and so wind from sea is constricted and must increase in speed	This applies to coastal valleys and coombes but not normally to coastal cliff sites
(6) An anabatic wind setting in	Anabatics induce light winds up sides in the sun or up cliff faces. Afternoon anabatics occur when sun moves round and illuminates new slopes previously in shadow	Only light wind regimes will allow anabatics. If anabatic direction is opposed to gradient wind then stalemate can induce calms	Keep an eye on the patterns of sunlight and shadow on local heights that communicate with your site. These remarks only really apply to the afternoon and not to the evening
(7) A katabatic wind setting in	A breeze springs up from a mountain or hillside and may help to oust a S–B that is blowing	Slopes that have been in sunlight are now shadowed and cool. The air sinks and drains off the hill sides	As (6) above but katabatics are far more likely than anabatics. Chances increase as afternoon gives way to evening
(8) A valley wind setting in	Valley wind can add to any S–B and make it stronger	The valley wind needs an extensive valley looking into mountains	See (4.3:A) (7)

Note also section (5) and (8) of (4.3:A)

5

HOW GLIDERS FLY

Of all sports, taking to the air demands that you have a fair idea of what you are doing before you start. It is important to understand the basics of how your craft flies so you can quickly put right things that may go wrong. We can understand some of the root concepts from sailplanes. These are rigid, and anyone can look at a sailplane and tell you where the centre line of the fuselage must be. However, you cannot do that with either hang gliders or parafoils. In fig. 5.1 the centre line of the fuselage of a sailplane is a reference to define what is meant by the angle of incidence of the wing. The inset shows what is meant by the chord line of the wing.

Since any glider has to sink as it flies in still air, the airstream comes up to meet the wing at an angle of attack (the angle of attack is evident from fig. 5.1). Angle of attack is the basic reference for airflow direction in hang gliders and paragliders which have no fuselage to give a line of reference; angle of incidence has no meaning for such gliders.

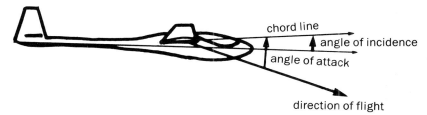

Fig. 5.1 In a sailplane which has a rigid fuselage the angle of incidence has meaning. The diagram also illustrates angle of attack and chord line

A pilot wants to do two things in a glider – go forwards and stay up as long as possible. As you fly, you are conscious of going forwards, but you are not so conscious of going down. That is why you need a variometer to tell you your rate of sink. Rate of sink is a velocity and in fig. 5.2 it is V_v while the forward velocity is V_h. But where does forward velocity come from, especially as there is no motive power? The answer is – from gravity. But, again, how

Fig. 5.2a The forces on a glider and their components. In steady flight L_h and D_h should be equal, but the latter has been extended for clarity

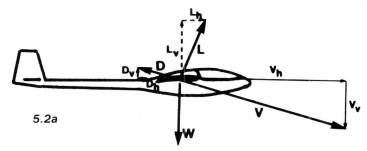

can a well-behaved force like gravity, which always acts straight downwards towards the centre of the earth, provide forward motion? To understand this we must, before we can go any further, take on board the ideas behind the components of a force.

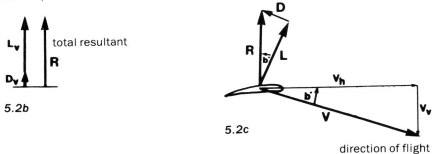

5.2b

5.2c

direction of flight

Fig. 5.2b The total resultant R must oppose the weight W and be in the same straight line. But the lift L is perpendicular to the direction of flight, so it is its vertical component plus the vertical component of the drag that make up the total resultant

Fig. 5.2c How the lift L, the drag D and the total resultant R form a right-angled triangle, whose hypotenuse is R

Components of forces

This idea can be understood by using a familiar object as an example – a wheelbarrow. We can firstly pull the wheelbarrow along the ground with a horizontal force H (see fig. 5.3a). It can then be upended and held up with a vertical force V (see fig. 5.3b). In practice, however, neither of these things is done: the wheelbarrow is pulled with a force F somewhere between the two (see fig. 5.3c). By doing that, part of H (h) makes it trundle over the ground and part of V (v) slightly reduces the weight of the barrow; both these parts are provided by F, h and v can be found via a diagram such as fig. 5.3d, but then care has to be taken. There now seem to be three forces (F, h and v), whereas there was only one (F) before. The rule is that you can either have F on its own or h and v together, but not both at the same time. The forces h and v are called the 'components' of F, and these components are used whenever there is a force which is not in a direction of interest to a pilot.

The idea is not confined to forces but to any quantity which is a vector. You can usually find out quite easily whether a quantity is a vector. If you naturally would draw an arrow to represent it in a diagram, then it is a vector. So, velocity is a vector, but energy is not – nor is temperature.

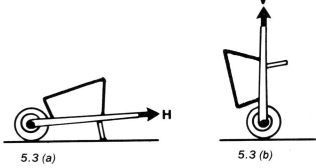

5.3 (a)   **5.3 (b)**

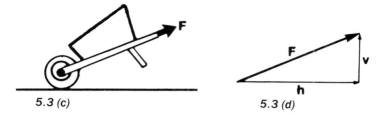

Fig. 5.3 To illustrate the idea of components of a force. Note that in (d) there are not three forces. We can either have F or v and h together, but not both at the same time

Forces acting on a glider

There are only three forces acting on a glider. They are:
   (1) weight (W) – always acting straight down
   (2) lift (L) – acting perpendicular to the direction of flight
   (3) drag (D) – acting against the direction of flight.
Because L is not in the same line as W, the vertical component of the lift L_v must be found. This acts directly against W and the horizontal component L_h which will provide foward velocity. At the same time, the drag is not in the same line as W and provides a small component D_v to add to the vertical component of the lift (see fig. 5.2a).

When the vertical contributions of lift and drag are added, R is the total resultant which, when the glider sinks at a steady rate of V_v through the air, must equal the weight W (see fig. 5.2b).

So the glider is now in equilibrium in the vertical, but what about the horizontal? The horizontal component of lift L_h drives the glider forwards, giving it a horizontal velocity V_h, but that velocity induces a drag component D_h. When the drag component equals the lift component, the glider flies forwards at a steady velocity V_h (D is over–emphasised in fig. 5.2a for clarity): the vector triangles which contain L and D and V_h and V_v have the same angle b°, so L/D must equal V_h/V_v (see fig. 5.2c).

The glider is now flying forwards and downwards at steady rates. The forward velocity is often called the 'penetration' and the glider can be more or less stationary above a point on the Earth's surface, but it can still have a penetration when the wind blows against the direction of flight. It is only the airspeed with respect to the glider that matters from the point of view of flying the aircraft. Wind speed over the Earth's surface only becomes important at take–off and landing and when, for instance, you are trying to stay within the compass of your launch site.

Glide ratio

It is a very important quantity for all gliders and is the ratio lift/drag. Sailplanes may have glide ratios of 40:1 while typical values for hang gliders are around 10:1, and at the bottom of the list come paragliders with values close to 5:1. This is a direct commentary on the efficiency of the three kinds of glider and is reflected in their comparative prices. The values quoted above are maximum values when the glider is making the best penetration it can with the smallest sink rate.

Polar curves

The glide ratio is the same as the ratio of penetration to sink rate and it can be seen why from fig. 5.2c, together with a polar curve. Glide ratios can be plotted on so-called polar curves and these curves give a great deal of information about the flying characteristics of the glider type to which they refer.

Draw two sets of axes as in fig. 5.4. The horizontal axis is the penetration speed (in ft/s in this case (but it could be m/s or mph or knots) while the downward vertical axis is the sink rate (in the same units as the penetration speed)). In this case the guinea pig is a hang glider. With suitable instrumentation it is found that when penetrating at 20 ft/s the sink rate is 4 ft/s. A pilot cannot fly slower than this or the aircraft will stall. This gives a point S on the polar diagram. When the glider is flown faster, the sink rate can be noted until the aircraft is gaining speed (50 ft/s) only at the expense of an unacceptable rate of sink (10 ft/s) at T. Somewhere in between these two extremes there is a speed of penetration which gives the least rate of sink (M). In this case the glider is flying forwards at 30 ft/s and only losing 3 ft/s in height. This is the maximum glide ratio for the glider and, being 30/3, gives a maximum glide ratio of 10:1. Note that the glide ratio can be found by drawing a line from the origin O just to kiss the curve at M.

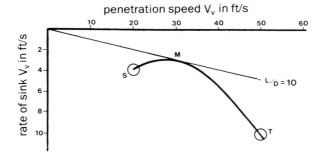

Fig. 5.4 To illustrate a polar curve and the way to find the penetration speed for minimum sink rate

The polar curves for the three types of glider are shown in fig. 5.5 which is based on one in *ABC of Paragliding* by Hubert Aupetit (Editions Retine). For sailplanes and hang gliders the maximum glide ratio (or just the glide) is found by drawing the tangent to their polar curves as described above. For paragliders it is found close to maximum penetration speed.

Headwinds and tailwinds

For some paragliders the maximum penetration speed may be more than 10 mph (15 ft/s or 5 m/s) above the best glide speed. If a polar curve is drawn for such a paraglider (see fig. 5.6), the effects of headwinds and tailwinds can be seen. With such a low-performance craft as a parafoil, the range of wind speeds in which you can fly is very limited and at first should not exceed 10 mph. However, it is no use looking at the TV weather forecast and assuming that the wind given will apply to your site. Read chapters 3 and 4 for some hints on assessing the true state of the airstream that is likely to affect your flying area.

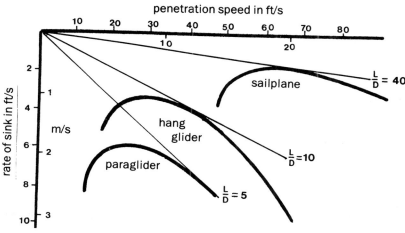

Fig. 5.5 Typical polar curves for a sailplane, a hang glider and a paraglider, showing their relative efficiencies expressed by their glide ratios

Assume, as in fig. 5.6, that your best glide speed is about 18 mph. This is just under 16 knots. Note that, for most purposes, if you have a quoted speed in mph, just reduce it a little to find the equivalent in knots. (You need to convert to knots, because the wind speeds given by met. services are in knots (1 knot = 1.15 mph).)

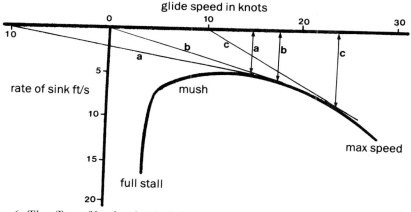

Fig. 5.6 The effects of head and tail winds on a paraglider

Imagine that the wind speed in which you fly is 10 knots. Flying directly into this wind will mean your ground speed is just under 6 knots. Your rate of sink is going to be the same as in still air, which means the angle of glide will steepen very considerably. Compared with the ground, you will be coming down at a steep angle. Contemplate what would happen should the wind increase to 16 knots while you continue to fly at your best glide speed of the same 16 knots. The ground observer would see you descending downwards at your rate of sink. This would continue until you ran into the wind shear (slowing down towards the Earth's surface). Assuming your penetration speed remained the same, you would still have a steep but decreasing angle of glide as you came down to the deck.

Obviously in headwinds you need to fly faster (and, conversely, in tailwinds, slower) than the best penetration speed for still air. How you work out what is best is shown in fig. 5.6. A 10-knot headwind means you start on the penetration speed axis at 10 and draw the tangent to the curve from there. For the case shown you need to fly about as fast as you can. However, with the wind behind you, it effectively adds 10 knots to your penetration speed and now the tangent kisses the curve at a point a little slower than in still air.

The facts that emerge are:

(1) with tailwinds, fly a bit slower – your rate of sink will not change much

(2) with headwinds, fly a lot faster – your rate of sink will increase considerably.

Controlling speed in paragliders

The main lines and controls of a paraglider are shown in fig. 5.7. The brake lines are two in number – one for each hand – and are attached to the outer trailing edges of the canopy. The lines extend down through the harness and end in toggles, which are also the steering toggles. (Steering will be discussed later.)

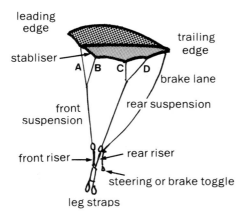

Fig. 5.7 The major parts of a paraglider

Pulling equally on both toggles will produce the same effect on the canopy as lowering flaps does on a rigid-wing aircraft. Lift increases, but drag is increased also. However, things are not quite the same with a paraglider. Certainly, drag increases and the canopy slows down. At the same time, lift increases but braking increases the angle of attack because you sink more rapidly. This decreases the lift as the parafoil is in partial stall with the new high angle of attack. The end result is that the lift does not go down very far with increasing angle of attack. Not, that is, until it is so large as to induce a full stall (see fig. 5.8). When it is in partial stall the parafoil is said to 'mush' and mushing is used to control rapid descent onto targets or into glades, or small areas generally. The likely flight paths when there is: (a) a headwind equal to the penetration speed; (b) a headwind less than penetration speed; and (c) a tailwind are shown in fig. 5.9.

The amount by which risers or brakes should be used is a matter for your instructors. No one can afford to learn to fly any form of aerial craft by trial and error, because the errors may result in injury or even death. However, it is worth noting that if no brakes are used,

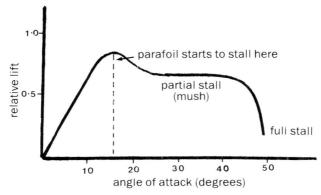

Fig. 5.8 How angle of attack leads to various classes of stall

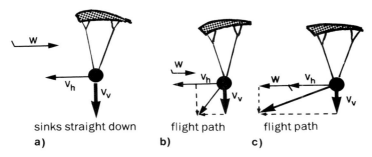

Fig. 5.9 How the flight path for a glider varies with the wind

the wing will fly at its fastest speed, but brake lines that are adjusted correctly for a light pilot will be found to be too short for a heavy one. If a pilot loses one or other of the toggles, it is not a disaster. In fact, the wing may fly better. Pull down equally on the rear risers to slow down and pull on the side towards which you wish to turn.

Turning a paraglider

Pilots of paragliders are like the bob-weights of pendulums and they obey the laws that Sir Isaac Newton laid down three hundred years ago. One of the consequences of these laws is that anything that turns in a circle must have a force applied to it directed towards the centre of the turning circle. If no sideways force acts, it goes straight on. Pulling a steering line, say to the left, all that will happen at first is that the pilot will go straight on while the canopy starts to turn left. This tendency to keep going in the same direction is called 'inertia'. To effect a turn, the lift of the canopy has somehow to pull the pilot into a circular path as well as maintaining height. It cannot, however, do both, so, in the moment the left brake line is pulled, there may be a slight gain of lift of the left extremity of the canopy, but the drag also increases and slows that side. The canopy swings left and, as that is what is watched from the ground, it appears that the pilot swings right. This puts force on the left riser and its lines, and the left side sinks. When, in a very short time, things settle down, the canopy pulls upwards and to the left, so providing the central force for the pilot to turn a left-handed circle.

As seen on page 39, the components of lift and drag add to produce a resultant force R which acts perpendicularly upward through the canopy (see fig. 5.10). The only other force is the weight W. If the paraglider continues its previous rate of sink (or something very closer to it), the vertical component (R_v) of this resultant will equal the weight, while there will be an unopposed horizontal component (R_h) that will lead to motion towards the centre of the turning circle.

If you are unfamiliar with these vector diagrams, note that vector triangles like the one above the canopy in fig. 5.10 are only drawn there to find the relative sizes of the components. The force R_h does not act there, but through the centre of gravity of the whole set-up. It is a rule with vectors that having found out how long they are and in which direction they point, you can then move them wherever you like so long as you preserve their length and their direction. So, R_h is found from the triangle, but is then moved to G, the point through which it acts. As pointed out before, there are not two R_h forces – only the one that acts through G. In the vertical direction there is the R_v force upwards and the weight force, W, downwards, and that is all.

Roll stability

You will see from fig. 5.10 that R_v and W are not in the same vertical line, and so there is always a righting movement trying to turn the canopy back to the horizontal. This is, of course, what will happen if the braking action on the left wing is not maintained. This shows at once that a paraglider pilot has carefully to hold on to his braking action through-out the turn, or level flight will soon be restored. This extreme roll stability is unlike other forms of glider. There, once the attitude of bank has been established, the controls can be centralised and the bank will be maintained.

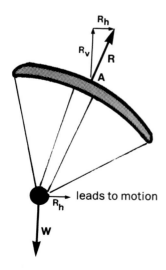

Fig. 5.10 How a paraglider executes a turn

G-forces

As the canopy is pulling upwards and inwards, it will seem to the pilot that he weighs more than he does in level flight. This increase in apparent weight is called a 'G-force' and is well-known on funfair machines like roller coasters where your stomach tries to get into your boots as you pull out from a 'dive'. You also experience a similar effect in a car which is driven too fast over a hump-backed bridge. That way, your stomach tries to get into your chest. It is all tied up with Newton again. You experience the unpleasant effects of 'G' because, in accordance with Newton's First Law of Motion, any material object such as the parts of the body will resist any change in the direction of their motion. Organs, like the stomach, that are not rigidly attached to the bony frame will continue to go straight on while the rest of the body goes elsewhere, carried by the harness that supports it.

Your instructors will tell you how to control the turns of paragliders so that you do not get into potentially dangerous tight spirals, but it is worth noting that a 50° angle of bank will increase your apparent weight by half so that in total you experience 1.5 G.

Let a dangerous spiral turn swing you out at greater angles and the G-forces increase rapidly. Below 45° the increase in G is not marked. Also, up to this angle, the increase in sink and penetration speed is small and can often be ignored. Thus normal turns in paragliding will not produce any great feeling of extra weight nor lead to catastrophic loss of height.

Controlling a hang glider

This is a matter of shifting your weight. The pilot redistributes his weight and, being below the centre of gravity of the wing, can change the wing's attitude.

The motions required are what one might expect. Pull forwards on the control bar (see fig. 5.11) to reduce the angle of attack and so fly faster. Pull forwards still further and the glider will dive. To slow the glider down, push backwards and increase the angle of attack, but do not go too far or the craft will stall.

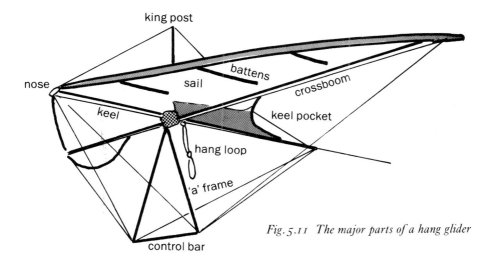

Fig. 5.11 The major parts of a hang glider

To turn, the pilot shifts to the required direction, say right. This places extra load on the wing on the right side and, because the airframe is more or less flexible, produces some slackness in the sail. The extra slackness is called 'billow'. At the same time the left wing tightens. A tight wing is more efficient than one with billow and so develops more lift, thus raising that wing and inducing a bank. The induced tendency to sideslip is checked by the keel pocket, by the billow itself and by any fins that are fitted.

While moving his weight to the right has induced an angle of bank for the pilot, the glider is not turning. To produce a turn as well as a bank, the pilot must shift his weight aft by pushing on the control bar. The result is that the nose lifts and leads the machine into a right-hand turn. Just as with paragliders the speed needs to be kept up in turns, because the stalling speed decreases rapidly with angle of bank. If the pilot enters a turn too slowly, the net result may well be a sharp stall and no real turn at all.

These are only the most basic points of control; your instructors will amplify them and make sure you know how to apply them correctly for the glider you are flying. The control of sailplanes is very close to the control of any light rigid-wing aircraft and is adequately covered in textbooks on gliding. Therefore, it will not be outlined here. As you progress in proficiency on whatever craft you fly, there is no substitute for good instruction – listening to and learning from an expert you can trust – and for hands-on experience.

Where lift comes from

Lift is a force generated by streamline flow. The enemy of streamline flow, and so of lift, is turbulence. Streamline flow is as smooth as the designers can make it and it is destroyed by several factors including too great an angle of attack and foreign bodies such as dust, dirt and moisture on the aerofoil surfaces.

When, as in fig. 5.12, two streamlines A and B are forced to separate by an aerofoil which has camber, then the A streamline over the top surface has to travel further in the same time than the B streamline. If this were not so, a partial vacuum would occur near the trailing edge T.

The energy of the air along a streamline is (in this case) made up of two factors. There is pressure energy (PE) and kinetic energy (KE), the latter increasing as the square of the velocity. The theorem due to Bernouille tells us that :

$$PE = KE = constant$$

which means that as KE increases so PE decreases.

air speeds (more K.E.)

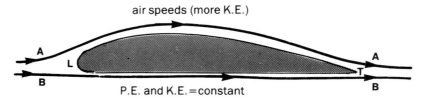

P.E. and K.E.=constant

Fig. 5.12 How a wing with camber generates lift by forcing streamline A to travel further than B in the same time

As the A streamline had to travel further in the same time, the velocity of the air along it had to increase, i.e. its KE increased while that of B hardly altered. Thus the pressure energy over the top surface decreased to keep the sum of PE and KE constant. That under the lower surface did not change appreciably, as it travelled in roughly a straight line.

As pressure is force per unit area, so the force on the lower surface is greater than on the top surface, and the wing is pushed up by the difference. It can be seen that the force can be increased by increasing the camber and increasing the wing area.

Stalling

With a rigid-wing aircraft the effective camber can be increased by using flaps, but flaps are not practical for hang or paragliders. On the other hand, parafoils, being non-rigid, can be given greater camber by pulling down on the back risers or the brake toggles. This, however, increases the parafoil's angle of attack and eventually makes it stall. In a stall the smooth airflow over the top surface breaks down to turbulent flow as shown in fig. 5.13.

Fig. 5.13 To illustrate the airflow when a wing (in this case a parafoil) stalls

Also, unlike the case shown in fig. 5.12 (which only applies to a powered aircraft), the glider is always presenting an angle of attack even though the aerofoil may be horizontal. This follows because of the ever-present rate of sink which makes the relative airflow upward as shown in the figure.

The stall in paragliders is a very personal affair, because it happens only at one angle of attack and at a quite definite stall speed which not only depends on the design of the parafoil but also on the weight of the pilot. It is to be avoided at all costs, as it results in loss of airspeed, loss of altitude, loss of control and possible collapse of the canopy. Your instructors will be very careful to point out how to avoid stalling.

6
FLYING WINDS

When the wind blows over and around obstacles, eddies are induced in it and the air becomes turbulent. Turbulence extends upwards as high as the wind speed and the stability will allow. In a stable airstream (as occurs in the early morning or the evening) the eddies are not helped by thermals and so the turbulent layer may be only a matter of hundreds or perhaps even tens of feet deep. Yet when the sun induces thermals, the depth of the turbulent layer goes up to thousands of feet. Thus in the morning, before the sun is able to heat low ground effectively, air riders over a slope facing the sun can find themselves in air that is turbulent to a much greater depth than that over adjacent low ground.

Roughness and mixing

The degree of roughness of a surface obviously depends on the nature of the terrain. Fig. 2.2 illustrates that, given a stable airstream, the air is mixed up to a greater height over the land than over the sea. Those who fly the cliffs will be in a zone where the turbulently mixed deck will change from a relatively smooth sea regime to that of the much rougher land, and so will become deeper.

A table will illustrate the point and give you an idea of how deep the 'mixing depth' may be in any given set of circumstances. It refers firstly to 'normal' conditions. This means that there is a normal degree of instability such as occurs on most of the days when flying is undertaken. Conditions will be normal when cumulus develops to a few thousand feet, but not, say, to as much as eight thousand feet or more. Conditions will be stable when an inversion limits the mixing to a depth somewhat less than the figures given in the following table (depths are in feet).

TABLE 6.1

Normal conditions			Stable conditions		
Wind force	Land	Sea	Wind force	Land	Sea
1	500	300	1	220	100
2	1200	700	2	700	350
3	2000	1300	3	1200	800
4	3000	2000	4	1700	1200
5	4000	3000	5	2200	1700
6	5000	4000	6	2700	2200

In dry airstreams cumulus clouds will not necessarily develop. There can still be normal conditions under blue skies even in the middle of the day. It is very likely that the 'normal' day will be relatively cool, especially in the early morning. Very hot days with little or no cloud can induce dangerous flying conditions, because of the 'explosive' low-level thermals that occur when an over-stressed atmosphere tries to break upwards through an impenetrable subsidence inversion. The latter is the strongest but the least likely form of inversion. It is far more likely that flying will take place under the normal overnight inversion. Recognising that inversions exist will have a profound effect on your flying.

About inversions

There is a temperature inversion of some kind almost every night. Even strong winds tend to be less strong overnight and it is the establishment of inversions that makes the surface wind speed go down from late afternoon onwards. So, the effect is there with winds of all strengths. However, it is most noticeable in lighter winds.

In chapter 2 it was explained that the normal state of the atmosphere is for the temperature to decrease with height. An inversion of temperature is something which is unnatural in that going upwards through an inversion layer the temperature increases (or at least remains more or less constant). Air near the surface loses or gains temperature by contact with the ground and for now that can be accepted as an immutable rule.

Due to day-time mixing, the warmth of the ground is transported up by turbulent eddies (see fig. 2.3). This happens through the depth of the layer that is mixed (see table 6.1 above). However, it is the sun which provides the warmth. When, through the late afternoon, it starts to sink, the natural radiation from the ground begins to lower the ground temperature (see fig. 2.4). This follows because the sun can no longer put in enough heat to counteract the loss by radiation. The temperature changes that occur near the ground during a normal day are due to a war between sunshine, which is trying to raise the temperature, and the Earth's radiation, which is always trying to lower it.

While the ground temperature does what you would expect and is highest at local midday and lowest at dawn, the air temperature lags on that by an hour or so. Thus the air is warmest during the early afternoon and is coldest a couple of hours after dawn. The way ground and air change their temperature during a normal day of fair weather is shown in fig. 6.2. These changes are collectively known as the 'diurnal' (i.e. daily) variation and they affect not only temperature but the surface wind speed and the amount of cloud that develops as well.

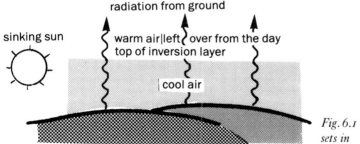

Fig. 6.1 *How an inversion sets in*

For some hours after dawn and until the sun is some 30° above the horizon, the overnight inversion acts like a lid on the lowest deck of the atmosphere and inhibits upward movement of air. This prevents the air at and below inversion height from being brought down by eddies. Thus the wind has died overnight, because mixing has been hindered. This needs explanation.

Daily changes in wind speed

It is a truism that wind speed increases with height. Whatever may happen at altitude, it is certainly the case that wind, which is slowed down by the friction of the terrain, must increase as you ascend. However, the mixing depth given in table 6.1 shows how deeply this effect extends. Table 6.1 really shows how much of the lowest air-deck is affected by the ground. Chunks of the wind anywhere between the top and bottom of the mixed layer can be transported to the surface without losing either their speed or their direction. This is how the wind becomes variable in speed and direction, with the sudden increases (gusts) being due to a parcel of wind from higher up barging into the slower surface wind. This cannot help but speed up the surface wind as a whole.

When an overnight inversion exists, as it can right up to the middle of the morning (or later in some cases), only turbulent eddies can mix up the deck below the inversion layer, and so the wind remains light. Yet as soon as the sun can heat the ground enough to induce strong thermals these punch through the inversion and suddenly you will feel the wind increase. Very often it will shift its direction clockwise (veer) at the same time.

So, the usual way the surface wind behaves on a good flying moring is to be light and fairly constant in direction up to the time when the inversion breaks, and from then on to increase. This increase will normally continue right through lunch-time into the afternoon. This is because, as the day progresses, deeper and deeper mixing hauls down faster and faster wind from the top of the mixed layer.

Daily changes in air temperature

Typical changes in the air temperature when the night is fine and the day is fair are shown in fig. 6.3. Around dawn the ground has cooled the air to well below its temperature at 1000ft and there is an inversion. By mid-afternoon the ground has warmed the air to such a temperature that it will be cooling faster than the natural rate (the Dry Adiabatic Lapse Rate (DALR)) as you rise through the first 1000ft or so. This is called a super adiabatic lapse rate and may lead to difficult lift conditions near the ground.

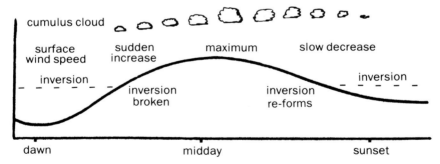

Fig. 6.2   The daily (diurnal) changes in temperature, stability and cloud

In the illustration the slope of the DALR is given for comparison and in this example thermal bubbles warmed to 65°F would stop rising at around 3000ft, but this does not allow for the slower cooling as the air rises through cloud. If, in this simple example, we took account of that we would find that the cloud tops would be higher than this. However, the purpose of the diagram is not to explain cumulus formation, but to show lapse rates near the ground on a normal flying day. Use a ruler to move the slope of the DALR around;

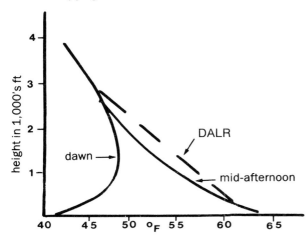

Fig. 6.3 Typical temperature profiles for a sunny mid-afternoon and a clear dawn compared with the Dry Adiabatic Lapse Rate

you will see that in the morning when the air temperature has risen to 50°F the air can only rise to about 500 feet because of the inversion.

Wind in the flying deck

The morning regime of the surface has been described, but what about up above in the flying deck? Let's start around breakfast-time when the inversion (that set in yesterday evening) is still there.

It's useful to remember that in the short term an airstream has to maintain its energy; should it lose energy in one part, it will increase its energy somewhere else in order to make up the difference. Thus when, from late afternoon onwards, the surface wind speed falls below a developing inversion layer it follows that the wind above the inversion must speed up to compensate.

The Eiffel Tower in Paris is 1000 feet high and a comparison between the wind speeds measured during twenty-four hours by an anemometer at its top with one in the local Parc St. Maur shows at once how the high-level wind goes down with the day when the low-level wind increases. By night the reverse happens: as the surface wind lulls, so the wind above speeds up to compensate (see fig. 6.4).

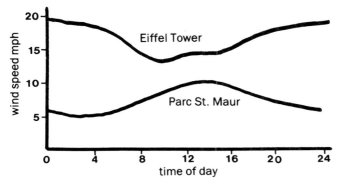

Fig. 6.4 Wind statistics for the top of the Eiffel Tower prove that when the surface wind goes down, the wind at 1000ft goes up, and vice versa

Thus night-time inversions will normally have faster winds above them than below them (see fig. 6.5). The effect of this is sometimes seen as wave patterns in stratocumulus and other types of cloud that form in inversion layers. There can often be a difference in direction as well. It is because of the arrival on the ground of the higher speed wind previously locked away above the inversion that the wind suddenly picks up in the morning after a quiet night.

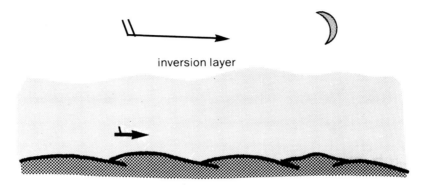

inversion layer

Fig. 6.5 The wind near the surface slows when mixing stops, while the wind above the inversion speeds up to compensate

The breaking of the inversion can be monitored by looking around for the first signs of cumulus. These will develop over the most likely spots for thermals. The first Cu will normally be seen over slopes facing the sun and Cu will begin to develop over lower ground not long after showing that the inversion is finally disappearing for good.

From now on the mixing process gathers pace so that faster and more variable wind will be found within a couple of thousand feet of the ground. There will also be thermal lift, as well as thermal sink between the thermals. Previously, only mechanical lift was worth looking for along the ridges or over the cliff edges.

When mixing gets underway, the wind speed at Cu height will become less while that near the surface becomes stronger. In this way the wind throughout the mixed layer will tend to come to a more equal speed throughout its depth. It will also become more equal in direction between the top and the bottom of the layer.

This process reaches its maximum development by about two hours after local noon; it remains like this for another couple of hours or so and then more or less rapidly decays as the inversion process starts. Now the variability in the wind decreases as well, and one of the best regimes for paraglider pilots is to be found over a slope facing north-west on a summer evening. In a smoothly-flowing stabilising NW wind, with the evening sun maintaining some thermal lift, flight can be sustained for a long period, even if no great altitude is possible.

It is useful to look at an actual example of what happens when an inversion sets in at the ground (see fig. 6.6). This one began at 1600 hrs. Up to that time the air temperature at 4 feet above the ground was higher than that at 150 feet. After that the cooling of the ground reversed this situation and a surface inversion was created. The difference between the 'warm' air at 150ft and the 'cold' air at 4ft increased throughout the night until, soon after dawn, it began to decrease rapidly and by 0900 the inversion was breaking down.

By taking an anemogram of the hour and a half after the initiation of the inversion, it can

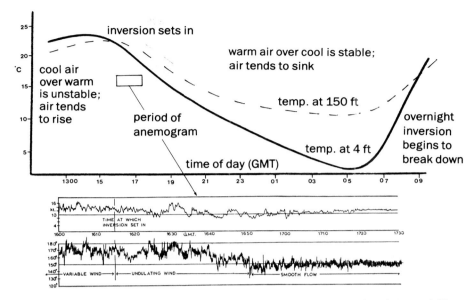

Fig. 6.6 How the inversion sets in late afternoon and how the wind goes from being variable to smooth flow

be seen clearly how a variable wind became one with undulations in it for about half an hour and then within an hour of the initiation it had become a smooth wind with very few variations. Note also how the wind speed followed suit, going from a mean of 14 knots to 10 to 12 knots and, as the night wore on, it would tend more and more towards calm. Winds that were stronger than this in the afternoon would obviously take longer to diminish and might not become as smooth-flowing as in this example. However, the example has all the ingredients of what normally happens, especially after fair-weather flying days.

As the sun sinks, and throughout the following hours of darkness, the depth of the air-deck under the inversion will increase. As it does so, the surface wind has only its own momentum to sustain it and, deprived of the help of faster wind from above, it dies. It will not pick up again until the morning sun starts to break the inversion or possibly a tightening pressure gradient sweeps away the current light weather regime. During the night there will be nocturnal winds, especially in hilly areas, and these must not be taken to indicate that the pressure gradient is tightening.

Summary of wind and weather changes on a normal flying day

Wind speed near the surface – increases through the morning and into the afternoon. Then decreases through the late afternoon and evening.

Wind speed in the flying deck – usually considerably faster above an inversion, but becomes much more even through the middle of the day.

Heap cloud development – nil until the inversion breaks. Then increases into the middle of the afternoon until inversion begins to reform. Then gradually dies out. Base of heap cloud rises through the day.

Wind direction changes in the flying deck

We become aware from looking at TV weather forecasts of how the wind blows along the isobars. However, if we consider the depth of the flying deck to be the same as the mixing depth given in table 6.1, the wind only blows in the isobar direction at the top of the flying deck. Near the surface of the ground the wind blows across the isobars at an angle which may be as little as 20° or as much as 45° on occasions. The usually accepted angle is 30° over the land, but only 15° over the sea (see fig. 6.7).

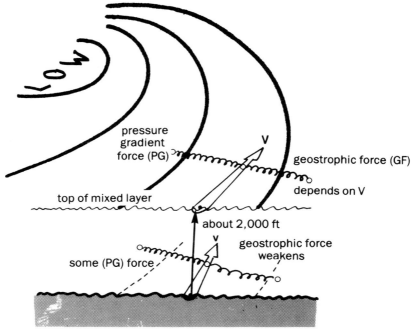

Fig. 6.7 Why the surface wind blows at an angle to the isobars

In the Northern Hemisphere, away from the tropics, surface winds blow out of high pressure centres and into low pressure ones in much the way shown in fig. 3.6. The atmosphere thereby maintains a continuous cycling of air in that highs are regions of sinking air and this air then flows out and into lows which are regions of rising air. The return flow is achieved at high altitude.

The wind direction at the top of the mixed layer is shown by the isobars and will blow to keep LOW pressure on its LEFT (Northern Hemisphere). The wind direction at the bottom of the layer will be backed to this (i.e. shifted anti-clockwise) by the angles given above. Thus as you ascend through the mixed layer, the wind direction has to shift and as it also will increase in speed so there will be two factors which have to be compensated for if you wish to remain in the best position relative to your take-off point.

The effect will be most marked if and when you can use mechanical lift to ascend in stable conditions. This follows because it is in stable conditions that there is most likely to be a wide divergence between the wind in which you take off and the wind as you ascend. When thermals are aiding the turbulence to create a deep mixed layer, there is going to be correspondingly less difference between wind direction at the surface and near the top of the mixed layer. However, in this case there will be considerable variations in the rate of sink as you enter and leave thermal zones.

Assessing the wind

If you fly from an established site, there may well be a windsock or even an instrumented anemometer to give you the take-off wind direction and speed. If not, then you have to assess these factors for yourself and table 6.2 should help.

It is also important to get an idea of what the wind is doing up there in the flying deck. In light wind conditions nothing gives a better indication of direction than what, in the early days of flying, was called a 'smudge fire'. In these 'green' days bonfires are less prevalent than they used to be, but smoke from a fire can be seen from altitude and can, by the way it rises, give pointers to the degree of stability. The same is true of factory or cooling tower plumes. Being more extensive and well off the ground, these give excellent indications of wind direction and the degree of stability. If the plume first of all rises and then sinks to the horizontal, the air is stable. If it goes up in a progressive arc, it indicates a degree of instability and if it grows into little billows that, before they disperse, resemble Cu clouds, it may well show a marked degree of instability. All these, however, only indicate the state of the air at the level of the plume. What is going on above is much more difficult to assess.

You can get a good idea of the wind speed at maybe a thousand feet or so aloft by observing the highest wind speed being recorded by an anemometer. Actually, you want to take the mean of the gust speeds, i.e. the average of the highest speed reached every time the wind suddenly increases. It may not be all that important to get an exact figure – a rough estimate will do – but certainly it is the highest speeds you have to assess as the wind rises and falls, rises and falls. If you do not have an anemometer, you can compare what happens to flags, leaves, etc. when the wind blows at its strongest. The variability comes because of mixing, continually bringing down chunks of the faster wind from higher up (you can get an idea of how high from table 6.1). Is the speed you assess this way greater or close to your maximum penetration speed? If it is, then should you fly? When ridge soaring with a hang glider or paraglider, it is very dangerous to fly downwind of the ridge. You must have enough penetration speed over and above the wind speed in order to stay within the lift band and not to be blown behind the ridge where turbulence and downdraughts can induce a stall.

Do not forget to allow in your flight plan for the clockwise shift in direction that occurs as you ascend, especially if you intend to be on the top of the stack of gliders. This shift may well be greater in the morning than in the afternoon, but it does rather depend on meteorological conditions of which you may not be aware.

Why the wind direction shifts with height

It may help to understand why the wind direction at the surface is angled in to the left of its direction at the top of the mixed layer. The reason is as follows. The wind at the top of the mixed layer is called the gradient wind and it blows in the same direction as the isobars on a weather map. It does this because there are two equal and opposite forces acting on it. One is the so-called geostrophic force (GF) due to the rotation of the Earth, while the other is the pressure gradient force (PG force) (see fig. 6.7).

TABLE 6.2 TO ESTABLISH WIND SPEED FOR FLYING

Description	Speed limits	Effects on gliders	Assessment points	Likely wind aloft
Light or gentle breezes.	2–10 knots Beaufort force 3 or less.	Para and hang glider pilots learn in these wind speeds. Good Cu streets with higher speeds. Possible danger from developing Cu at lower speeds as strong updraughts may develop.	At 2–3 knots smoke just drifts. But wind vanes and socks do not respond. If the wind can be felt on the face then it is 4–6 knots. Now vanes respond. Light flags do not extend. Exposed water ripples. At 7–10 knots light flags and streamers extend. Wind socks are reliable. Tree leaves will audibly rustle and be constantly in motion.	3–15 knots at 1000ft. (Upper values when surface wind at top of bracket and if climbing to 2000ft).
Moderate breezes.	11–16 knots Beaufort force 4.	Hang gliders can penetrate against these wind speeds but paragliders may not make ground speed. Afternoon speeds on days of good Cu development.	At top of this range most flags extend fully. Small branches move. Dust and loose paper may be raised. If on the coast there are frequent white horses to be seen.	15–20 kts if wind off the sea. 20–25 kts if wind comes over land.
Fresh breezes.	17–21 knots Beaufort force 5.	Limits of wind speed for paragliders and then only at low level, with heavy pilots. Hang gliders can still make useful ground speed if they accept a high sink rate.	Small trees in the open will sway. Look to the tops of trees for a more universal indication – they will be in very noticeable motion. On the coast there are moderate waves with many white horses.	25–30 kts if straight off the sea. 30–40 kts if wind comes fully over land. (Upper values at 2000ft).

Above these speeds sailplane pilots will be flying but hang gliders will need unacceptable rates of sink to make forward ground speed.

When a wind first starts to blow, it will do so from high towards low pressure. That is what you would expect, but the effect of the Earth's rotation produces a kind of centrifugal force. Once the wind has been in existence for six hours or so it ends up apparently thrown to the right of its path in direct opposition to the PG force that is trying to make it move directly from high to low pressure. This means that the wind also blows parallel to the lines of equal pressure (the isobars) that define the slope or gradient of pressure.

The PG force will be the same through all the levels you will fly, but the geostrophic force varies with the wind speed – lower speed means smaller GF. Imagine that the wind vector is an arrow pivoted at its tail end and is held between two springs (as in fig. 6.7). At the top of the mixed layer (what may be called 'isobar height') the two springs exert equal force and so the wind vector looks along the tramlines of the isobars. Down below, near the surface, the wind is slowed by friction and so the GF force is weaker but the PG force is still the same. The spring representing the GF force is also weaker, and the wind arrow is therefore pulled sideways and does not blow along but across the isobars, out of higher into lower pressure.

This explanation shows that when the terrain is rough the angle between the wind for take-off and that which you experience higher up is going to be greater than when the terrain is smooth. It will change most in the first few tens of feet and then vary progressively less up to the top of the mixed layer.

It is worth looking at the results of actual measurement of wind speed made within 30ft (10m) of the ground (see fig. 6.8). The curves show how fast the wind increased with height

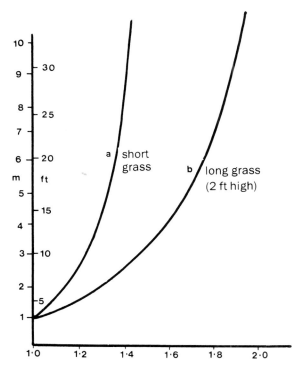

Fig. 6.8 How the wind varies in the first 30ft or so over a grass site

over (a) short grass, and (b) long grass about 2ft high compared with the speed at 3ft. So, take an example. If the wind you measure from a hand-held anemometer is, say, 10 knots and the site is well-cropped grass, from curve (a) it will be 14 knots at 30ft (10 x 1.4). If the site is rougher, with maybe the wind coming over a field of standing corn, from curve (b) the speed is almost doubled by the time 30ft (10 x 1.9 = 19kt) is reached.

From this it can be seen that most of the wind increase occurs within the first 30ft of the ground over grassy or similar sites: the curves have become very steep by the time they get to this height and so there will be only a slow increase above it. However, if your site is bedevilled by thickets and copses or up-wind woods, etc. the deck in which this major increase occurs will be deeper or perhaps broken up into zones by the air having to flow over and round objects. A rough rule of thumb is that mechanical turbulence will extend to about 3h where h is the average height of the objects hampering the wind.

If inversions exist not far from the ground, as they can in the early evening when stability is setting in, the angle between the take-off wind and that at, say, 200-300ft may be as high as 45°. An extreme case occurs when flying a coastal site in which the surface wind is seabreeze and only a hundred feet or less above the wind can be diammetrically opposite, i.e. an off-shore wind.

By definition, hang gliding and paragliding will be from slopes, edges and other elevations, so the effects of the topography on the wind near the surface can be vastly more important than the effect outlined above (see chapter 8).

Portraits of clouds
The pictures are chosen to bring out useful points of recognition for cloud types that have specific meaning for glider pilots.
(1) Cirrus crossed by an exhaust trail with broken stratocumulus below
Cirrus is ice-crystal cloud and shows no shadows (compare with the lower water-clouds). This form runs as much as twenty-four hours before the arrival of the worst of the frontal weather. It is associated with a jet stream which, while not visible itself, tends to show up in the speed of movement in the Ci (or the trail) and also in the direction in which the cirrus banners lie. This is much the same as that of the accompanying jet.
(2) Cirrostratus with some thin altostratus forming below it
The halo about the sun proves immediately that this is cirrostratus. No other cloud produces ring haloes in this way. The altostratus is revealed by the two sun-dogs – patches of light on opposite sides of the sun and at the same level – which only form in water-drop clouds. When this cloud appears following Ci, it becomes more certain that bad weather is on the way.
(3) Altostratus with stratus pannus below
The altostratus is often a flat muddy-grey sheet with very few features. When pannus forms below it, rain is about to commence. The pannus will rapidly cover the sky and maybe the hill tops as well. When As follows Ci and Cs in sequence, you can then truly believe that a warm front (or an occlusion) is responsible.
(4) Nimbostratus seen as a front clears
Often Ns cannot be seen directly, as it hides below the low layer of pannus beneath it. However, that is academic: long periods of continuous rain (or snow) come from nimbostratus.
(5) Altocumulus lenticularis
This is the correct name for lens-shaped clouds which develop in the rising parts of the waves that are induced in stable airstreams by hill and mountain ridges. Such clouds also occur at low level (Sc lent) and at cirrus levels (Cc lent).
(6) Altocumulus castellanus and floccus
These two clouds are often seen together, and presage thundery weather to come. The floccus are the cumulus-like lumps in the foreground while the castellanus is the lines of cloud with turret-tips in the background. These lines form along the wind direction at their level.
(7) Cumulus seen in the afternoon when the base has risen to maybe 300–400 ft. These are formed into streets moving downwind from some thermal source. Note the uniform base and tops of these fair-weather clouds. There are no whisps of cloud hanging below them, as occurs below the cumulus of seabreeze fronts.
(8) Stratus of a humid airstream covers the hills and mountains in Wales
This cloud can form very suddenly and any signs of its appearance over the higher slopes should be a signal to curtail flying.
(9) Stratocumulus in the warm sector of a depression
In the background is the approaching cloud-line of a cold front. Note how there is a clear space just ahead of the front. This is due to sinking air compensating for the updraughts in the frontal clouds themselves. Time to be on the ground and secured against rain squalls, possible hail and thunder.
(10) Big showers approaching from the Welsh mountains somewhere on the English border
Note the head on the left. It is the rounded cauliflower shape which goes with cumulonimbus in its heavy rain or hail stage. Also note the film of white cloud on its top. This is pileus and indicates strong updraughts. On the right the general solidity of the cloud structure plus the mass of false cirrus on the extreme right show that this group of showers mean business.

(11) A thunderstorm in the hail stage when it is at its most virulent
This cell will soon spread against the tropopause while a daughter cell (the growing head in the foreground) develops to take over the production of heavy rain, hail, thunder and lightning. In high places especially, precautions against getting struck by lightning should be taken.

(12) When a warm front approaches in hilly or mountainous districts the altostratus often becomes lenticular. Note the cirrostratus above, seen through the gap on the left, and altocumulus just visible through the wave-streaming hole, centre top. With time this will lose its fish-like shapes and become more like photograph 3.

(13) The sky before thundery outbreaks will often look like this. The lines of medium-level cloud in the lower foreground are altocumulus castellanus. These get their name from the turret-tops that grow out of the bands of cloud that lie along the wind at their level. Above these there is altocumulus floccus which may or may not get its name from looking like a flock of woolly sheep.

(14) The sky which often follows (13) looks typically like this. These are masses of medium-level cloud which is chaotic in appearance and the base is often crossed with dark skeins of lower cloud. Thunderstorms, whose bases are maybe as high as 10,000 feet, are developing above this cloudbase.

(15) It is important to recognise signs of what may look like humble Cu developing into something bigger. One of the most potent signs is pileus. This is a cap of fog-like cloud which forms over the tops of convective cloud that is growing very fast. The cloud in the picture does not look very deep, but it will soom become so as it lifts the air above it and forces it to become cloud. A similar event is occurring on the left of this cloud. The pileus is often left half-way up a developed Cb cloud as skeins of darker cloud.

(16) Wave-streaming produces lines of Sc across the wind in the evening. There may well be some lift to be had for those who can get that high.

(17) When wave cloud begins to look like flying saucers, then we are witnessing the effects of rotor streaming, as in the centre of this picture.

(18) The mountains can set off big showers when the rest of the airstream is clear of cloud. Here air from the Irish Sea is pushed up into Cb by the Snowdon range.

(19) A seabreeze front seen in its early stages of formation. It is the line of deeper cumulus in the lower part of the sky and we are looking seaward from not many miles inland. Here we have Sc inland from the front rather than Cu, but the Sc is broken and lets the sun through on to the land.

(20) When the air is dry the seabreeze frontal lift may produce most of the Cu cloud in the sky, as seen here from Bolberry Down near Salcombe, South Devon. Note that there is some Cu to be seen inland but none on the seaward (upper) side of the front.

(21) Portrait of a single cumulus cloud which is moving right to left. It shows the deeper trailing end and shallower leading end which goes with the idea of a circulation within it and under it.

(22) Cu develops in the sunshine behind a clearing cold front whose high cloud is disappearing off to the right. There's lift to be had now, but look out for showers developing before long.

(23) The division between no cloud on the seaward side and cloud on the landward side of a seabreeze front. This is more usual than the sparse line of Cu along the front in photograph 20.

(24) Waves develop in the interface between two different wind speeds above and below this Sc. The wind is perpendicular to the waves.

7
HEAP CLOUD DAYS

Heap clouds develop on days when the air has a polar origin. Such airstreams are cool and so will become unstable when they arrive over higher sea and land temperatures. Air brought south from polar seas will find itself over increasing sea temperatures and so will erupt into vast fleets of showers, most of which will dissipate over the ocean wastes.

However, on many occasions, especially in summer and autumn, the maritime Polar (mP) airmass brought down behind retreating depressions will continue to feed showers onto those coasts of Atlantic Europe which face the wind. At all times of year (except perhaps in mid-winter) this cool airstream will become unstable over the land, with the instability increasing into the afternoon as the temperature rises.

In satellite cloud pictures cumulus and cumulonimbus clouds that are sufficiently large will appear as groups of white dots often lying in lines (or streets) along the wind direction. In photograph 7.1, such a group is seen streaming down from Iceland towards Ireland and western Scotland in the rear of old hurricane Flossie on the evening of 16 September 1978.

7.1 Infra-red satellite cloud study from NOAA 5 showing how to recognize the influx of big shower clouds. Time 1941Z 16th September 1978

September is the time for old hurricanes to invade European shores and it is also when the sea temperatures are at their maximum. Cool polar air is bound to become very unstable as it is drawn south behind any form of low that crosses the British Isles. Each individual image dot need not be a single Cb cloud, because the satellite's radiometer cannot separate cloudmasses that lie within half a kilometre of one another and so if two or more individual clouds lie closely together they will be recorded as one.

Because of the immense number of showers that breed and die over northern seas, vast quantities of latent heat are released at altitude and this creates an inversion which eventually limits the convection until the cloud tops become the humble ones of fair-weather cumulus. Such lowly Cu are called 'cumulus humilis'. Often the cumulus airstream has travelled a very long distance over the Atlantic round the quasi-stationary low-pressure region that so often exists south of Iceland and it is this returning maritime Polar (rmP) airstream which usually gives the optimum conditions for gliding.

Cumulus days

These very often start off cool and clear, but it cannot be guaranteed that the cool, clear morning will not become more unstable as the day wears on. In these cases cumulus grows into the form called 'congestus' (see photograph 15) which does not actually produce showers at first but could well do so at any time. The up and downdraughts associated with congestus and cumulonimbus (shower clouds) can make for a dangerous set of flying conditions and are best avoided.

At first, the sun will raise the temperature until thermals can dissipate the overnight inversion, but the 'latent heat' inversion higher up will normally stop the upward motion of thermals, thereby keeping the cumulus of small vertical extent. However, as thermals gather strength, even the higher inversion can be broken and, as the air above it is likely to be unstable, so the thermal currents move off to higher realms and may reach 20,000 feet or more. Cumulonimbus clouds are the result and sometimes they develop sufficiently to produce thunderstorms. This effect can be enhanced by rising ground. For one thing, slopes on which the sun can shine more nearly perpendicularly will heat up more than lowlands and, for another, mechanical lift over ridges, etc. will sometimes be enough to set air, close to instability, into a truly unstable state.

Forecast showers

If showers are forecast for your site, it is pretty certain that they will actually occur somewhere in the *area* covered by the forecast. This means, of course, that you may not get them, even though big tops and anvils may be visible in the local airspace. However, in turn, you should not assume that your relatively clear sky is not being affected by them.

Shower clouds gather the updraughts to themselves, but spread the consequent downdraughts over quite a wide area around them. This is why showers usually occur in their own personal spaces, with blue breaks between. The blue breaks are where the air is sinking to compensate for the updraughts occurring in the cumulonimbus clouds. This is found just ahead of cold fronts where sinking air creates a slot of fair skies just ahead of the leading edge of the frontal cloud proper (see photograph 9); when no fronts are present, there can be airmass troughs which have the monopoly of the updraughts, leading to clearing skies both ahead and behind them. It is certainly worth asking why after showers are forecast the weather should remain stubbornly fair or even fine. The answer may well be that there is an airmass trough somewhere upwind.

The state of the air above the ground

This is difficult to determine for the layperson. Met. officers with their 'tephigrams' can see where the inversions, etc. are, but from your own observations only cloud tops or cloud layers can give you this vital piece of information. In summer, when the sun has enough power, a thin layer of Ac or As is often not sufficient to prevent thermals, and so Cu develops under the higher layer of cloud. There will be some thermal lift to be gained here unless you are after a height record. Sometimes the power of the sun can disperse the higher-level cloud, allowing the Cu to develop further in the afternoon – even as far as producing showers. At other times, Cu will develop below the semi-permanent holes that may appear in a much more extensive cloud sheet. These are to be expected in hilly districts where wave-streaming can occur.

These events are summarised in table 7.1 (Heap Cloud Days) (see pp. 64–5) and you should consult the table for help in suggesting the likely course of a flying day. It may look great now, but will it eventually turn out that way?

Formation of cumulus

As the sun rises in the sky and gets to work heating the land, it will not do so uniformly. It can be assumed that the sun needs to be striking the ground at an angle of about 30° or more before it is possible to set off thermals strongly enough to create Cu clouds. On an east-facing slope of, say, a fifteen- degree angle, the sun will be at 30° to that slope much earlier than on flat ground. Thus sun-facing slopes will generate Cu first and so presage their creation over lower ground. You can get an idea of when Cu are likely to start appearing over low ground from table 7.2.

TABLE 7.2 DATES AND TIMES AT WHICH SUN IS MORE THAN 30° ABOVE THE HORIZON

Latitude	Location	*Feb 18 and Oct 25*	*Mar 21 and Sep 23*	*Apr 21 and Aug 23*	*June 27*
58N	North Scotland, Skaggerak, North Baltic	Never higher than 20°	1030-1330	0830-1530	0700-1700
52N	Southern Ireland, Central Southern England, Holland	Never higher than 27°	0930-1430	0800-1600	0700-1700
46N	Central Biscay coast of France, North Adriatic	1030-1330	0900-1500	0800-1800	0700-1700
38N	Lisbon, toe of Italy, Southern Aegean	0930-1430	0830-1530	0800-1600	0700-1700

Factors which increase the chance of a piece of land being a good thermal source include the type and colour of the soil, whether it is ploughed or has a crop, and whether it is

TABLE 7.1 HEAP CLOUD DAYS

Typically these are fine around breakfast-time. The air should be fresh and the visibility good. If forecast goes for light winds and you are within thirty miles of a main sea coast, consider the possibility of seabreeze effects (page 87). Times are local sun times (LST).

General situation	Situation around 8–9 a.m. LST	Situation by midday	Afternoon situation	Late afternoon and evening situation	Remarks
Day when fair weather Cu exist for most of the day. Ridge pressure pattern most likely.	Fine, cool, wind between calm & 10 knots. No great change expected in pressure pattern during the day.	Good thermals from early if slopes face sun. Cu develops as wind increases. Wind often comes from a veered direction when it picks up. Often greatest gust factor of the day.	Thermals fully developed by mid-afternoon. Bases rise to 4000ft or more. Wind at maximum for the day. Gust factor lower because of increased wind speed.	Inversion sets in late afternoon. Cu begins to die away. Wind speed falls and backs as inversion forms. Wind becomes more laminar; flow and gust factor no longer a problem.	This is the classic 'fair' day. Yet showery days start the same way so check forecast in the morning before flying.
Day which is more unstable than above. Early Cu grow into showers later. Wind often around NW.	As above but wind may be moderate and early signs of possible showers are when whisps of low cloud build up early.	Inversion limits Cu at first but big Cu grow in early part of forenoon. Gust factor easily exceeded so fly early. There can be showers by as early as 10–11 a.m.	Strong thermal currents and towering Cu or Cb induce dangerous downdraughts near showers. Para and hang glider pilots should think carefully before flying.	Showers die out and heap clouds stabilise maybe leading to extensive Sc. Could be the best part of the day with last of thermals plus dynamic lift.	The forecast should warn of showers but unstable airstreams in hilly terrain can set off showers more easily than over low ground. Paraglider pilots setting off into the hills should beware.
Day when showers are forecast but forenoon stays remarkably fair.	As either of the above. Cu develops and maybe even a shower occurs.	Forenoon does not develop cloud as expected. It may seem odd if forecast went for showers. Look upwind for an airmass trough.	Airmass troughs develop late forenoon or early afternoon. May look like a cold front (Photo 9). Trough produces strong thermal turbulence lasting for an hour or so.	Skies usually clear behind these troughs but maybe showers can break out again by this time.	Expect airmass troughs inland away from sea coasts. They move with the wind across the country. Especially on NW winds.
Day when Cu develops and then spreads into extensive stratocumulus.	Often blue sky and there is no sure way of telling if Cu will remain individual or spread and amalgamate.	Cu that develop hit a developing inversion and spread into Sc. Thermals inhibited by cloud cover. Gust factor low.	Cloud cover may stick or holes develop, allowing some thermals. Look for gathering high cloud through any holes in low cloud cover.	Cloud sheet often breaks but may not do so. If it does disappear reason may be that a front is on its way.	This effect of Cu spreading is a sign of stabilising airstream. Reason is usually a front or a trough coming in.

Day when Cu develops below thin or broken layers of higher cloud.	Usually layers of thin Ac/As or/and Ci/Cs but can be high Sc with holes in it so letting the sun through partially.	Normally only between May and September when sun has enough power will Cu develop below the upper layer. Latter needs to have a base above 6000ft.	Sometimes the Cu will develop enough to punch up into the upper layer and create holes in it. Wave streaming may also create holes allowing better development of Cu in the clear spaces.	Cu will either die early or may spread into Sc below the higher layers.	There will be lift to be found but it will not be extensive. Gust factor usually low. Allow for the times when the higher layer 'burns off' with the day or disappears for some other reason leaving a normal kind of Cu afternoon.
Day when Cu develops in some areas even though the day is generally overcast.	Often a total cover of Sc which may appear to be too thick to allow thermals to develop. The cloud may also be either Ac or As.	During the forenoon some much brighter patches are to be seen. Under these there will be developing Cu. If you get into one of these 'holes' do not expect it to last.	Same remarks as for the forenoon but the chances of holes in the cloud sheet may be less. However, it is difficult to be at all precise about when and where the holes will appear.	Cloud may or may not clear with evening.	These 'holes' may be produced by fall streaks from cirrus cloud above. They may also be due to wave-streaming in which case they can be reliable for periods of an hour or so.
Day with sea-breeze fronts.					See chapter 9.

covered in woods or copses, etc. Large developed areas, such as towns, airfield runways and roads, can provide thermal sources, but must not suffer from too much disturbance, i.e. little-used country roads are in, but motorways are out. Having said this, a small degree of disturbance is required for a warmed bubble of air sitting over a thermal source to break away. Once it does break away, you have to imagine a great invisible hot-air balloon of rising air. From research it seems that one thermal is not sufficient to produce a full-sized Cu cloud, but that several, following in one another's wake, are required (see fig. 7.1).

Fig. 7.1 Diagram showing the normal way in which thermals take off and their structure when clear of the surface

Eventually, the rising thermals develop a kind of ring-doughnut shape, with ascending air through the centre and sinking air around the periphery. For soaring, it is the centre of these elusive thermals that has to be sought, as the rate of ascent of air in this part is twice that of the bubble as a whole. This can create a problem if several gliders find the rapidly rising air one after another. They will all arrive at the top of the thermal in a heap!

Thermals are usually invisible, but when the air is rising fast it can push the air above it into a filmy cap (much as developing Cu can create a pileus cap) that reveals where the maximum lift is to be found. Otherwise, the formation of the first wisps of what will rapidly become a Cu cloud is your first indication of where the thermal is and what its source may be.

Lift from thermal bubbles

Experience will show you that two airstreams at different temperatures do not mix when they blow over one another. When a bubble of warm air grows over a thermal source and before it separates from the ground, it acts as an invisible hillock pushing the wind over and around it. In such cases, lift may be found within tens of feet of the ground, although its source may not be apparent. The lift comes from the dynamic lift generated when the wind blows over the developing thermal bubble.

Lapse rates and cumulus

The bases and tops of cumulus appear where they do because of the lapse rates of ascending air and the shape of the change in temperature with height of the environment. A typical

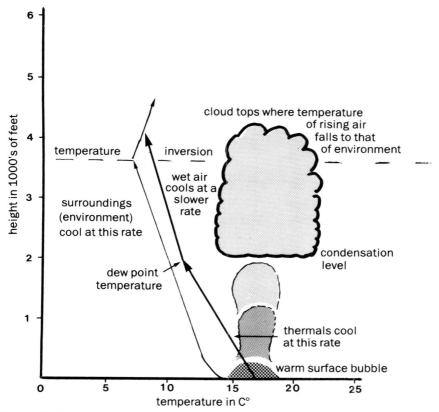

Fig. 7.2 To illustrate how thermals give rise to Cu clouds and what determines their base and tops

example is shown in fig. 7.2 where a thermal bubble is warmed to 17°C. This is 3° above the temperature of the environmental air. When the thermal bubble lifts off and rises, it cools at the Dry Adiabatic Lapse Rate (DALR). When the ascending air has cooled to the dewpoint of 11°C, it will begin to condense into cloud with a base of 2000ft. After this the air goes on ascending but at a slower rate (the Wet ALR), because the production of water droplets from vapour releases latent heat and slows the cooling.

Cloud streets

Eventually, the ascending air meets an inversion and, having come to the same temperature as its environment, stops rising. Thus the tops of the clouds are where rising air, cooling at its natural adiabatic rates, comes to the same temperature as its surroundings. As shown in fig. 7.1, when there is a wind, the thermal bubbles break away at an angle and, of course, the cumulus drifts off with the gradient wind. With a prolific thermal source to feed them, lines or streets of Cu form down the wind at their level. However, streets do not need such hot-spots when their tops are limited by an inversion as low as, say, 4000ft.

There will be lift under the lines of the cloud streets, but sinking air in the spaces between one cloud and the next and especially between one street and the next. These spaces will depend on the wind speed and the height of the cloud tops. If there is no wind, heap clouds tend to grow in spaces whose diameter is $2\sqrt{2h}$ where h is the height of the cloud tops. It is unusual for heap clouds to grow in zero wind, but it can happen when great sultry Cb clouds grow in heat lows over land in summer. The most massive and prolonged thunderstorms are the result.

It is normal for Cu clouds to grow in a wind which naturally increases in speed with height. Under these circumstances, which are the ones necessary for the formation of streets, the distance between one street and the next is 2h. These facts translate into distances as follows:

TABLE 7.3 DISTANCE IN MILES BETWEEN CONVECTIVE CELLS OR STREETS

Cloud top height	3000	4000	6000	10000	20000	30000	40000 feet
No wind	1.5	2	3	5	10	16	21
Light/wind	1	1.5	2	4	7.5	11	15

The air motion in a cloud street will be something like fig. 7.3 with, in this instance, thermal bubbles being induced by a heated hill slope and cloud tops at around 6000ft.

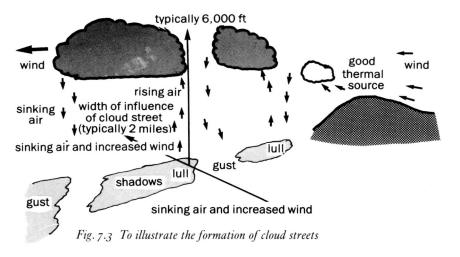

Fig. 7.3 To illustrate the formation of cloud streets

Gusts and lulls

The ring–doughnut shape of a thermal, illustrated in fig. 7.1, will lead to a cloud of much the same shape only when there is no wind. When Cu develops in a wind, it takes on the kind of shape shown in fig. 7.4 and a circulation develops, with warm thermal currents rising into the trailing end and cooler currents descending below the leading end. Because the wind is stronger at Cu height, the descending currents bring down this faster wind as gusts. The gust is a more or less sudden stab of wind which is thrust from above into the surface wind field. It will be less turbulent than true surface wind and can arrive out of the blue in the apparent lee of trees and buildings.

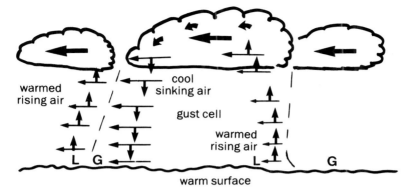

Fig. 7.4 Idealised gust cells. The rising and sinking currents must be superimposed on the horizontal air motion. G is where gusts are to be expected

As the Cu passes, the wind becomes slowed and more turbulent. This is the lull which usually follows a gust in a variable airstream, and is followed by another gust and so on. The time period between one gust and the next is typically of the order of a few minutes. The circulation, etc. constitutes a gust cell and gust cells chase one another across the countryside on any heap cloud day (see fig. 7.5). They are sometimes more regular and pronounced than at other times. However, imagining great ghost dirigibles of rising and sinking air whose size is something like the size of the Cu clouds that ride over them, as in fig. 7.4, can be useful in phasing your take–offs and landings to avoid the worst of the sudden gusts that occur.

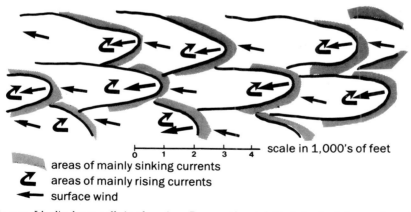

Fig. 7.5 Idealised gust cells in plan view. Because the air behind the shaded parts (gusts) is from above, it is normally veered to the direction it had where the air was rising

Gust factor

Because heap cloud days are the ones most sought after by glider pilots, your chances of meeting the gust-and-lull conditions described above are high. The rule of thumb needed for paragliders to indicate when the conditions are likely to be unsafe may be called the 'unsafe turbulence rule' or the 'gust factor'.

If the wind changes its speed by 4 knots in a period of 4 seconds or less, then it is unsafe for flying paragliders.

Failure to observe this rule can lead to control problems but, more dangerously, a portion of the canopy may collapse because of a gust.

Seeing the wind

It is possible to do this by using devices which draw a continuous record of the wind speed and direction. They are called anemographs and the charts they produce are anemograms. Fig. 7.6 shows the anemogram of four minutes of wind on a gusty day.

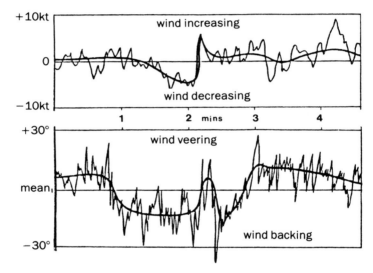

Fig. 7.6 To illustrate a typical gust-lull pattern in a normally variable wind. The wind tends to shift clockwise (veer) when it blows faster

The speed trace varies above and below the mean speed and, in fact, spends very little time at the mean speed. A variable wind usually blows for short periods faster than the mean speed and then reverts to blowing for about the same time at less than the mean speed.

By drawing a solid line through the minor variations (which are due to mechanical turbulence), it can bee seen that for the first minute or so the wind was above the mean speed but then towards 2 minutes it sank in speed (i.e. it lulled). This only made the sudden increase in speed all the more marked. (It is a good illustration of how normal gusts act. The circulation in a gust cell delivers a packet of stronger wind all of a sudden into the lulled surface wind.) This was certainly a dangerous gust for paragliders, as it exceeded the gust factor by a substantial margin. Such gusts are prevalent in unstable airstreams with Cu clouds and the latter need not be all that massive. There was an exactly opposite effect just after 3 minutes when the wind suddenly lulled by some 8 knots in as many seconds. That would also exceed the gust factor, even though it was the opposite of a gust. It was still a sudden change which could have been of such limited extent as to collapse one side of a canopy.

Looking at the direction trace, there are many spikey turbulent shifts in it which tend to mask what the wind was actually doing. For the first minute or so it blew mainly from the right of the mean direction (i.e. it was veered). Then, until the gust struck, it backed by more than 20°. Soon after, it backed temporarily before gradually shifting some 15° to the right of the mean direction. This habit of shifting clockwise when the gust strikes, only to go back for a short period to what it was before, is well known to those who sail boats and boards. It is called a 'gust tongue' and the real wind shift comes half a minute or so later. Usually the direction shifts are not as important to glider pilots as they are to dinghy sailors, but the speed changes certainly are. Speed changes that arrive so rapidly show that gusts are sharp–edged, sweeping down from cloud height through the flying deck and therefore easily able to affect one side and not the other of a parafoil or a hang glider sail. However, the hang glider, which does not rely so heavily on the throughput of air to the wing, will not be as troubled by gusts of this kind, but they can still pose some sort of threat when they happen as sharply as in this (typical) example of a gusty wind on an unstable day.

The glider pilot who is just about to land when the wind suddenly gusts or lulls will have his previously carefully judged approach thrown into confusion when either the wind suddenly increases or, maybe worse, suddenly decreases in speed by as much as 10 knots. A sudden shift of 30° or so (as occurred at 3 minutes) could also be a hazard to the beginning or intermediate pilot, if not to the expert. For these and other reasons, it is important to assess the degree of shiftiness in the wind and to realise that such shiftiness comes with most heap cloud days.

Abnormal wind patterns

Study of anemograms of some good flying winds (which in this case often have easterly components) shows an unusual pattern of increasing and decreasing wind strengths quite unlike the gust-lull pattern associated with unstable westerlies. In these abnormal air-streams the wind climbs in a series of steps (with lulls between) to a maximum, taking perhaps as much as ten minutes to complete the change. It remains at the higher speed (which is often only about 10 knots) for a minute or two and then begins to sink in steps to its minimum value. The whole pattern may repeat only after twenty minutes or more have passed, but sometimes it happens more quickly. Often these winds turn up on warm mornings with sunshine but still some rafts and islands of alto clouds about the sky. It is unusual for much Cu to develop.

Study of such winds that have preceded the onset of seabreezes on the south coast of England showed that sometimes the wind would be very spikey, with sudden increases to, say, 10 knots followed by equally sharp falls to close to calm. Such winds might well exceed the gust factor quite regularly and should be looked for. A light flag or a wind sock will indicate whether such an abormal series of speed changes is occurring, but you will need to take time out to study their antics over something like a 20-minute period. The flag or sock will alternately hang limply along the mast and soon after be fluttering, only to go back to its limp condition again shortly after. It must not be forgotten that these surface changes are being fed through the depth of the flying deck and so you must expect something similar to be happening in the air above you.

The wind direction changes that go with these very variable airstreams must not be ignored. There will sometimes be very wide shifts of direction in phase with the speed changes. However, they will act in exactly the opposite sense to those that come with the normal cumulus day's set of gusts and lulls. With abnormal wind patterns, when the wind is at its maximum speed (these cannot be called gusts), the direction will usually be backed to the mean wind direction and, conversely, as the speed drops to minimum, the wind will wanderingly veer.

8

WINDS OVER SLOPES, HILLS AND MOUNTAINS

Hang glider and paraglider pilots are going to fly from high places simply because gravity is their only means of power. Therefore, meteorological happenings in the hills and mountains will be of supreme importance to them. Most pilots look for a slope that:

(a) has a slope angle of 20–30 degrees that gently changes to flat ground (see fig. 8.1)

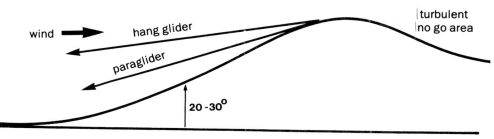

Fig. 8.1 The perfect hill slope for basic gliding and the no-go area

(b) faces the wind to within 30 degrees of the direct line onto the slope
(c) has no major obstructions for at least half a mile in the direction of the wind
(d) has a generally smooth surface so that wrenched ankles are less of a hazard on landing
(e) is not bedevilled by obstructions in the lee of the ridge or brow into which a pilot could be blown (see fig. 8.2)
(f) does not have any humps or hillocks to windward of the take-off slope which might produce turbulence or rollers in their lee (see fig. 8.2).

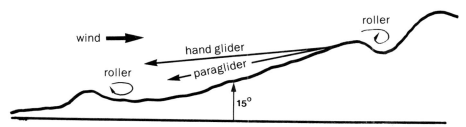

Fig. 8.2 A slope with problems. Any sizeable hillocks or depressions can induce rollers and other turbulence

Satisfying all these conditions probably constitutes having found the perfect site and, for beginners and improvers, they are virtually a must. However, when you have had some experience, you might take liberties with these conditions, although you may do so at your peril.

You can test the angle of slope with a clinometer; the angle can be less for a hang glider than for a paraglider, simply because the former has a better glide angle (see fig. 8.1).

The topography that will induce the least complications into the pattern of the airflow includes a ridge that faces the wind and is more or less straight and of a uniform height for perhaps a mile either side of where you intend to fly. Then you will have a sausage-shaped zone in which dynamic lift will be relatively uniform and safe. This zone is called the 'lift-band' and fig. 8.3 shows where it will occur and especially what its limits are. If the

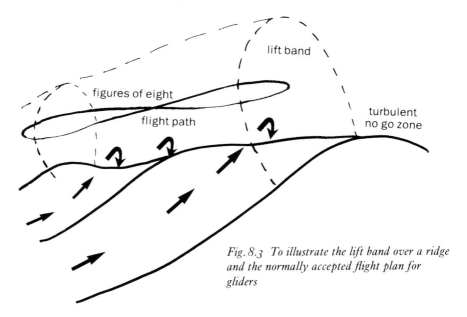

Fig. 8.3 To illustrate the lift band over a ridge and the normally accepted flight plan for gliders

ground in lee is flat or, worse, falls away, as shown, this is a no-go zone. You must make figure-of-eight flight paths along the ridge and within the lift-band, and on no account should you be driven into the no-go zone.

Windflow round isolated heights

The more isolated an eminence, the more problems it will produce, because the wind will not only have to blow up over it but also round it. This produces zones of deflected and increased wind in some places, with decreased wind in others.

To get an idea of what may happen, take an actual case study of an isolated hill, Blasheval Hill in Scotland. A perspective plot of the hill is shown in fig. 8.4a and how the wind varied across the hill top is shown in fig. 8.4b. It is particularly interesting to see how the wind speed falls most where the change from lowland to hill slope is most marked and is less when the contours lead to a smooth change. However, what fig. 8.4b shows best is the great increase in wind speed over the top, resulting in almost twice the undisturbed wind speed. What the actual changes in wind speed amounted to around the hill are shown in fig. 8.4c. It indicates how the wind speeds up all round the summit by a large factor of 1.5 or more, but the drop in the surroundings is quite small because, of course, it is spread over a much

8.4a

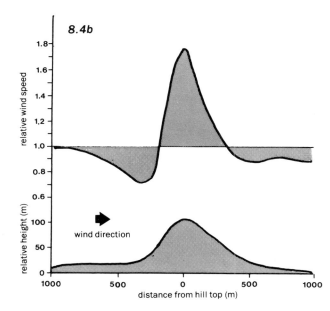

8.4b

Fig. 8.4 A study of Blasheval Hill in Scotland illustrates the way the wind will change its speed round an isolated hill or mountain. (a) is a perspective plot of the hill. (b) shows how the wind speed falls just ahead and behind the hill, but makes up for it by increasing markedly over the top. (c) shows the increase and decrease around the hill compared with the undisturbed wind

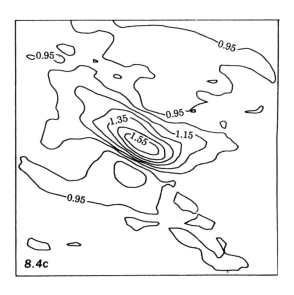

8.4c

larger area. However, it proves that if wind speeds up somewhere, it is bound to slow down somewhere else nearby or above.

What will happen in the flying deck above the level of launch? It must be remembered that the airflow over hills can induce wave clouds right up to cirrus heights (6 miles (10 km) or so), so there is literally no height that you can fly which will be free of the effects of the topography. However, calculations indicate the following changes in wind speed over the summit compared with the undisturbed wind.

Height in metres	10	25	50	100	200
Over-speeding %	120	68	42	22	8

So, it is as well to remember that seeking the up currents is fine, but what goes up must also come down somewhere else – and maybe you with it.

Windshifts in valleys and mountains

It is always useful in meteorology to look at what has actually occurred; fig. 8.5 shows what happened to the wind in an area of Wales near the Snowdon range. It was February, and winter winds tend to hug the contours more than summer ones. However, the lessons are clear.

At (A) is seen the effect of the land on the wind speed. Force 5 winds over the sea fall to Force 2 in very short distances.

At (B) a Force 4 wind from the sea is directed by the promontory, but it increases to Force 5 when it blows through the valley between two mountains.

At (C) is seen the way the wind in the open is W, but becomes directed NW by the run of the contours.

At (D) the wind is steered and slowed by steep slopes near the sea. The Force 3 wind from just N of W becomes Force 2 SW. Force 3 is induced by the wind blowing down the slopes of the mountains onto a lake, while in the neighbouring valley the wind is only Force 1. The very light wind is a local effect, but note that it is at right angles to the 'true' wind direction, which is the one over the sea.

It can be seen at (E) how a steep spur can split the wind so that it blows in two directions at right angles within a short distance of one another.

At (F) the 'free' wind of Force 5 NW seen at (A) is shifted W and then is slowed down and steered to blow through the Straits. The dot in a circle indicates that it was calm there.

At (G), once free of the drag of the mountains, the wind picks up again to Force 4 or 5, but its directions are still dictated by the way the land lies.

At (H) are seen the effects of valleys: how the winds tend to blow along the valleys, and sometimes are decreased and at others, increased.

This example of winds recorded at the same time over a wide mountain area shows that you can judge little or nothing about launch conditions from the wind over the lowlands. You largely have to take pot-luck when you get there and have actually to measure what is occurring.

The idea of conserving the energy of the airflow is very useful when thinking about the likely run of the wind around the heights and valleys. When the wind blows at an angle across a valley, as at (H) in fig. 8.5, its natural trend is to swing to blow along the axis of the valley. When the valley narrows – as almost all valleys do – the wind must increase where it

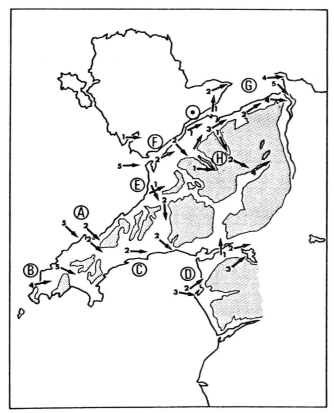

Fig. 8.5 A study of Northwest Wales illustrates the many things that can happen to winds in the mountains when the air is stable

is limited by the slopes on either side. But the wind above will at some point have to decrease in speed to keep the total energy of the airstream (on a broad front) the same as it was before the surface increase occurred. Remember that if you have found a relatively light wind patch but above you the clouds appear to be scudding by quite rapidly, you must expect to have a fight to penetrate the wind after take-off, as the wind aloft will be making up for its lack of energy near the surface.

Wave streaming

Wave streaming occurs when the whole airmass is more or less stable. Thus it is a feature of the mountain sky when a warm front or occlusion is approaching (see photograph 5). It can also occur in the warm sectors of depressions and will often go with warm conditions at any time of year. Four major types of streaming flow are shown in fig. 8.6.

(a) *Laminar streaming* simply makes the air lift over the ridges, but nothing much else happens. This kind of flow occurs when both wind and hills are gentle affairs. A gentle wind of tropical origin blowing over downland could result in laminar streaming.

(b) *Standing eddy streaming* occurs when the wind speed increases so that a large station-

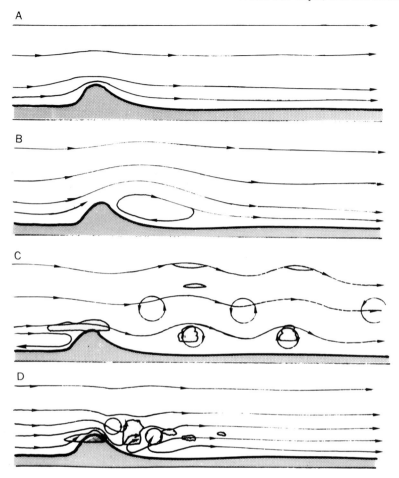

Fig. 8.6 Four kinds of streaming. (a) laminar streaming when the hill ridge is gentle and the wind speed is low. (b) standing eddy streaming with retrograde winds in lee. The wind is stronger than in (a). (c) wave streaming recognised by lenticular cloud formation and maybe including downwind rollers. (d) rotor streaming recognised by roll clouds and turbulent motions in downwind cloud stacks. The wind is quite strong in both the latter cases

ary eddy appears in lee of the ridge. When prospecting a slope for launching be careful that you are not being fooled by the upslope component of a standing eddy of another ridge further upwind. Look at the direction of motion of any low-to medium-level clouds and, if they are moving in a widely different direction from the surface wind, then think twice about launching into that wind.

   (c) *Wave streaming* produces the lenticular clouds so characteristic of the mountain sky. Many things may happen and not all of them need be there at once. There can be an eddy on the windward side of the ridge and the latter is often under a cloud called a 'helm bar'. Roll clouds occur 2 to 20 miles (3 to 32km) downwind of the ridge which needs to be much more massive than downland. Again, surface winds blow against the general run of the airstream under rollers, and there may be invisible rollers at greater altitude. Lenticular clouds will build up to cirrus levels, but they are most prominent in the medium levels (above and below 10000ft). The wind speed needs to be greater than for either (a) or (b), but this is the most prevalent form of streaming. However, it must be restated that not all of these effects have to be present when the tell-tale lens-shaped clouds appear. For instance, rollers do not have to be present, although strange phenomena occur with wave streaming. Sausages of lenticularis will not move across the sky in the way we expect clouds to do. This is because the waveform of the airflow is not changing its wavelength; the clouds are formed where the air rises and they evaporate away again where the air sinks. However, wave patterns do not remain constant for very long in most instances, so that lenticularis may move forwards or even back against the wind. On some rare occasions a cloud element may literally 'jump' back nearer the ridge as the airflow rearranges itself.

(d) *Rotor streaming* is the most violent form of streaming and needs a large massif and a fresh or even strong wind. Now there is a highly turbulent zone in lee of the ridge, with strange contra-moving clouds in the violent rotors, etc. which occur. The airstream may well be wetter than that for (c) and so the helm bar sits down on the ridge more closely than at other times.

What you have to contend with when rollers develop in a wave streaming pattern can be illustrated through some actual observations at Ronaldsway airport on the Isle of Man. The airfield is approximately 4 miles (6.5km) from a substantial ridge; in fig. 8.7 roll clouds

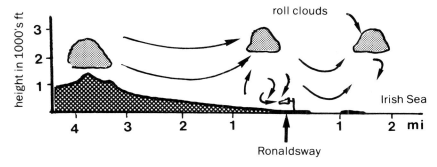

Fig. 8.7 To illustrate the effect of wave streaming at Ronaldsway Airport on the Isle of Man

developed over the field and further on over the Irish Sea. The way the wind went all round the clock and was sometimes calm and at others as high as 15kt is easily seen from table 8.1 (see p.80). However, what is most striking is what can happen within just half a mile. For example, at 0736 while the wind at the control tower was northerly that at the wind sock half a mile to the east was south-westerly. That it would be totally foolhardy to think of flying while such conditions exist almost goes without saying.

Flow over cliffs

This can be the source of a wonderful experience or the means of producing a disaster. In his book *ABC of Paragliding*, Hubert Aupetit tells of a twenty-two mile (35.5km) flight he made along the massive cliffs that lie between Le Havre and Étretat on the north-west coast of France. He describes the dynamic lift he experienced from the on-shore 15 to 20 knot

TABLE 8.1 AN EXAMPLE OF ROTOR STREAMING AT RONALDSWAY AIRPORT

Time	Wind at control tower	Wind half a mile east
0700	S 15kt	no observations at this time
0716	calm	ditto
0728	a full 360° rotation	ditto
0731	SE 14	N 14
0736	N 10	SW 9
0741	SW 6	N 14
0748	ENE 14	N 5
0752	calm	N 14
0754	W 10	N 9
0802	SW 10	N 14
0808	E 6	NW 9
0824	calm	NW 9

wind and the problem zones, such as the gaps where there are river estuaries or, on a smaller scale, where there have been cliff-falls in the past. Such zones have to be crossed from a vantage point of sufficient height to allow for the lack of lift over these indentations. He points out the wisdom of not trying to take off where the wind speed is enhanced by being constricted to blow up a fissure from the sea.

It was afternoon and so the sun shone on these west- to north-west-facing cliffs, producing thermals in the W to NW wind. Such wind directions are well-known to be inherently unstable, so everything was in his favour and he stayed aloft for hours, sometimes grazing the cliff edges, sometimes being forced down towards the sea, but the conditions were such that he could always find enough lift to get back up again. His drive to the coast was under much convective cloud and through quite a few showers, but he was confident that this was all due to the heating of the land and that the coast would be fine – which it was.

The cliffs along the Sussex coast of England between Beachy Head and Seaford are a favourite place for gliding enthusiasts. They are good for morning flying, because they face the sun and a W to NW wind, when light, can be turned into an on-shore seabreeze quite early. This, now southerly, breeze has, in its lowest layers, all the instability characteristics of the W or NW wind it displaced. Dynamic and thermal lift will combine to produce great soaring flight in the lift band over and just to seaward of the cliff edge. As pointed out in chapter 9, the seabreeze is essentially stable but not in the first hundred or so feet. There is still room for limited convection under the seabreeze's 'lid'. Also, the seabreeze effect clears the cloud from the coastal strip and ensures that the full effect of the sun is felt on the cliff faces.

Wherever the seagulls soar on effortless wings there has to be a lift band, but it is important to realise that a covering of clouds such as stratocumulus or, worse, stratus will leave you with only dynamic lift and no help at all from convection.

On-shore wind-flow

This needs to be studied when the seabreeze blows or on overcast days that suggest stable or even sinking air. There can be considerable changes in wind speed and direction as the ground-hugging wind seeks to get ashore through the gaps to avoid going over the heights. On unstable days its own natural buoyancy will carry it up over the obstacles in its path, although the lowest layers will still do their best to funnel through the gaps formed by the

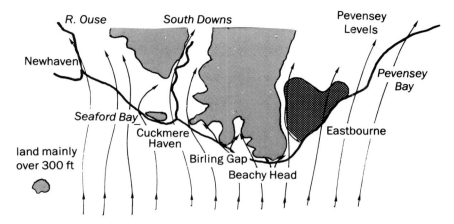

Fig. 8.8 Likely on-shore flow of seabreeze or other stable southerly air around Beachy Head and surrounding high outcrops of the South Downs

river estuaries. Again taking the Sussex coast between Newhaven and Beachy Head, fig. 8.8 shows the likely flow of a seabreeze. The place from where the gliders take off will be somewhat starved of air and so you have to expect enhanced wind speed as you attempt to penetrate the edges of the high grounds.

Winds over lakes and valleys

These will be modified whenever the weather is fair and the general winds are light. Inland waters tend to remain cold and so there will always be a tendency for a lake breeze to develop towards the sides which are in the sun. In fig. 8.9 (see p.82) a typical long, narrow 'finger' lake is orientated so that one side sees the sun early while the other is in shadow. Thermals over the sunlit slopes (A) will have to be replaced by an on-shore lake breeze which in its turn has to be fed either by sinking air over the lake itself or from the shadowed slopes (B). Sometimes a street of cumulus will appear over the sunlit slopes. This lake breeze will slacken as the sun moves round and begins to leave the (A) slopes in shadow while the (B) slopes begin to see the sun. This will lead to stalemate over the lake, with neither side having the advantage. As a result, the Cu may disappear for a time but may reform over the (B) side later.

Only through careful study of the direction in which a lake or valley faces and experience of its relation to the sun during the day can the dynamic and thermal lift over slopes such as (A) be taken advantage of. Do not expect good lift in the morning, say, to be anything but short-lived. You may be lucky, but the tendency is for the lift zones where mountains and valleys exist always to be changing and, therefore, not to be reliable.

Mountain and valley winds

Valley and mountain winds are due to unequal heating of valley sides and of the slopes that rise into the mountains at the heads of the valleys. The regime, which is prevalent in the Alpine valleys, for example, can be best understood from fig. 8.10 (see p.83). The early

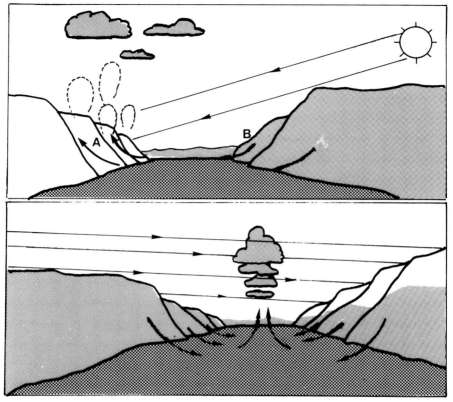

Fig. 8.9 How a lake or valley breeze is generated by anabatics and katabatics (a) in the morning and (b) in the late afternoon

morning is characterised by air draining from the mountain slopes down the valleys, often to arrive over a lake (A). This night wind falls during the early morning, but there will then be thermal lift over the sunlit slopes (B). The anabatic winds strengthen during the afternoon and take air from the valley floors which has to be replaced by a wind blowing up the valley towards the mountains (C). Once this wind gets going (D), and even though the sun deserts the slopes and the anabatics die out, the valley wind continues to blow into the evening under its own very considerable momentum (E). At this time the only lift to be found will be dynamic and over spurs that penetrate out into the valley wind. It may well be completely negated by sinking katabatics.

What happens during the night is only of academic interest, but suffice to say that the mountain wind sets in during the middle of the night and will still be with the early birds (F, G and H).

Mountain-gap winds

These are winds which blow through the passes and the cols between mountain peaks. The best known is the Mistral of the French Mediterranean coast. The wind is known by many

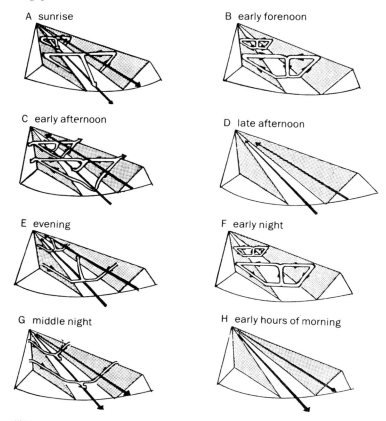

A sunrise

B early forenoon

C early afternoon

D late afternoon

E evening

F early night

G middle night

H early hours of morning

Fig. 8.10 The phases in the growth and decay of mountain and valley winds

names from the Spanish side of the border all the way to Genoa on the Italian side. These all reflect the wind's masterly ability to sweep away any other winds there may be and to impose its own, often violent, regime.

When the isobars are orientated for winds to blow over the Alps, the Massif Central and the Pyrenees, etc., these barriers present a formidable obstacle to the wind which becomes dry and cool, bursts through the gaps, and falls like a very strong katabatic wind down any valley path that presents itself. Anyone flying in these areas must ensure they listen to the forecasts, as there is no time of year when Mistral is absent from the zone between Perpignan and Genoa, and quite often it is gale force, especially where constricted by any narrowing of the valley path it is following. Table 8.2 gives the average number of days on which Mistral can be expected between Perpignan and Marseille, as well as its strength.

TABLE 8.2

	Jan	Feb	Mar	Apr	May	Jun	Jul	Aug	Sep	Oct	Nov	Dec
Force 6	10	9	13	12	8	9	9	7	5	5	7	10
Force 7	8	6	10	9	6	4	4	3	2	2	3	7
Force 8	6	6	9	4	3	2	2	2	2	0	0	5

Apart from August and October/November, there are normally one or two days when Mistral blows at greater than 20 knots along the whole of the above coastal strip.

A similar well-known wind is the Bora of the Yugoslavian coast of the Adriatic Sea. Here the mountain barrier is mainly the Dinaric Alps, but similar strong to gale dry winds will blow off the Dolomites towards Venice and, as the 'borino', off the Appenine backbone of Italy. In fact, the mountain flyer should remember that winds like the mistral and the bora are just the big brothers of similar winds wherever mountain barriers stand athwart the large-scale winds.

Föhn winds

Such winds often come suddenly after abnormally clear conditions have prevailed. They are at their most formidable on the Alpine Foreland (where they are known as Föhn) and in the lee of the Rockies (where they become the Chinnook). In the case of the Alpine barrier, the wind has to be blowing from the Mediterranean side and is, on that side, often warm and stable (see fig. 8.11). The Alps present a very real obstacle to these winds, which may

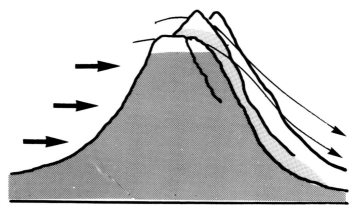

Fig. 8.11   To illustrate the way a frustrated airflow eventually bursts through the passes as a Föhn wind

take days to develop sufficient potential to burst through the passes and descend the valleys in lee as strong blustery falling winds. They are very dry winds, having lost much of their moisture on the windward slopes of the mountains.

How such Föhn winds actually flow is shown in fig. 8.12: the Thunersee (T) experiences gale-force Föhn from southerly points (S). The lower left-hand lake is the Brienzersee, with Interlaken lying between them.

The Föhn has a psychological effect which is important to recognise. It has been shown, for instance, that road accidents increase markedly before and during Föhn outbreaks, and surgeons even delay operations when Föhn threatens, as they tend to be more accident-prone at such times. There is certainly a lesson here for those who wish to ride the Alpine air, and anyone who flies in mountains must always get as much help as possible from the established met. services. It is also extremely important to realise that, while Föhn and Chinnook make the headlines because of their strength and viciousness, such winds can

Fig. 8.12 A case-study of the way Föhn will descend through the valleys, maybe being enhanced by constrictions

occur in the lee of any formidable mountain barrier. For example, Aberdeen on the east coast of Scotland and under the lee of the mountains, gets Föhn with locally increased temperatures; the effect is also known on the north-west coast of England when, as happens sometimes, stable NE or E winds blow over the Pennines.

Enough has been said about the potential dangers to flyers in the mountains. Mountains are where flyers will always go to experience the elevation and the thrills; all they should do is take fewer chances with the weather in this type of terrain than elsewhere.

9
SEABREEZES AND NOCTURNAL WINDS

Seabreezes are a natural coastal wind and it is possible for a seabreeze to blow any day between April and September. Those who fly the cliffs during this period will experience winds from seaward on most days. This is no coincidence – the days that favour gliding are also the ones that favour seabreezes!

The best seabreeze days have mornings when the breakfast-time winds are less than 10 knots and the rest of the morning is clear and relatively cool for the time of year. There will not normally be any low cloud at first, so the sun has a maximum chance to warm up the land, but there may well be islands and rafts of alto and cirro clouds scattered around the sky. The seabreeze has to have sun on the land before it can start, because that is its power source. So, overcast mornings will not produce breezes.

In case there is any doubt about it, seabreezes are not just any old wind from the sea. A seabreeze has to be generated by the land surface being warmed above the temperature of the adjacent sea. It is normal on any coast for the land temperatures to exceed the sea temperature on almost all days between April and September. It can also do so outside these months. There can be light seabreezes on more or less calm days in February and March, but they are the exception rather than the rule. At the autumn end of the normal seabreeze season you can have seabreezes invading the coastal strip on light-wind days, but again they are few and far between. It is more likely that breezes will blow in late winter than in late autumn, and you can almost discount them in December and January.

It must be realised that reference is being made here to breezes around the shores of Britain and Atlantic Europe within the same bounds of latitude. Go further south towards (or into) the Mediterranean and breezes become stronger, and are thus able to overcome winds that are in the moderate or even fresh bracket (10 to 20 knots) when these blow from land to sea in the mornings.

Some research I undertook into the frequency of seabreezes during the years 1959-61 proves what has just been said. It was done at Thorney Island airfield in the centre of the south coast of England. It is about 3 miles (5km) inland from the main sea coast (see fig. 9.3, p.90). These figures did not necessarily include all the days when breezes blew, because there could have been breezes that were only just strong enough to invade the coast but which never got quite as far as Thorney.

TABLE 9.1.

Months	Jan	Feb	Mar	Apr	May	Jun	Jul	Aug	Sep	Oct	Nov	Dec
Average number of days	2	2	6	9	13	15	14	12	12	5	1	1

This proves that half the days of the high months of May, June and July are likely to see seabreezes; in July 1959 there were, in fact, no less than 21 days when seabreezes crossed Thorney's airfield. That was an exceptional month, but it shows how prevalent seabreeze effects can be.

The fact that this was some thirty years ago does not matter – weather does not change much in such a relatively short period.

Seabreeze effects can be explained by using some examples. Hang glider and paraglider pilots who fly the cliffs at Beachy Head or some other similarly high south coast location will be given mechanical lift by the seabreeze during most flying days, even when the morning wind starts by blowing off the land. If it should remain from landward, flying would be out, but the thoughtful seabreeze blows in to make it not only a possible flying day but a good one.

In general, cliffs that face east on an east coast or south on a south coast will give excellent flying conditions, because with the sun full on them the cliff faces will produce thermal lift which, for most of the time, will be aided by on-shore seabreeze to add mechanical lift. West-facing cliffs do not see the sun until well into the afternoon and,'similarly, west-facing hill slopes inland do not get the full effect of the sun until afternoon either. Thus west coast heights are for afternoon and evening flying, while east coast ones are not likely to sustain lift into the late afternoon and evening. Slopes that are steep down towards the sea and face NW will make evening flying possible almost up to sunset in mid-summer.

The seabreeze near the coast

It is important that the coastal flyer understands the mechanism of the seabreeze so that sinking currents which could make for a dangerous landing in the water can be avoided.

The weather situation on the mornings of seabreeze days needs to supply the following:

(1) little or no low cloud in the hours surrounding breakfast-time

(2a) wind speed below 7-8 knots when the direction is such that the wind blows towards the sea. This direction may be 45° either side of the direct line to the sea. For example, on a south coast the wind could be anywhere between NW and NE

(2b) speed similar (but could be stronger) when the direction is such that the wind blows roughly parallel to the main sea coast

(2c) any speed when the wind already blows from the sea

(3) a fresh cool feel to the morning so that it seems likely that heap clouds will develop later. Very warm mornings with an oppressive feel to them will be highly stable and will engender sluggish breezes.

What happens when the wind blows gently from the land in the morning is that over the strip of sea just off the coast it will be reduced to calm by the force which will eventually produce a seabreeze (see fig. 9.1a).

Sometime during the morning – as early as 8 or 9 o'clock local sun time (LST) when calm, but as late as early afternoon if the wind is stronger – the breeze will begin to blow lightly and fitfully from the sea (see fig. 9.1b). It will be aided by convection currents up cliffs that are fully in sunlight, so there may be a local cliff breeze before there is any seabreeze proper.

It will not take long to strengthen and, providing the forecast does not go for a big wind increase during the day, it will be with you right through into late afternoon (see fig. 9.1c). On the south and east coasts of England the breeze blows at maybe 12-15 knots over the coastline and between 6 and 10 knots when it gets inland.

Once established, the seabreeze forms a stable deck with few major variations in speed or direction. It will, like most winds, strengthen somewhat through the middle of the afternoon and will, unlike the majority of winds, tend to veer with time (i.e. to shift clockwise) so

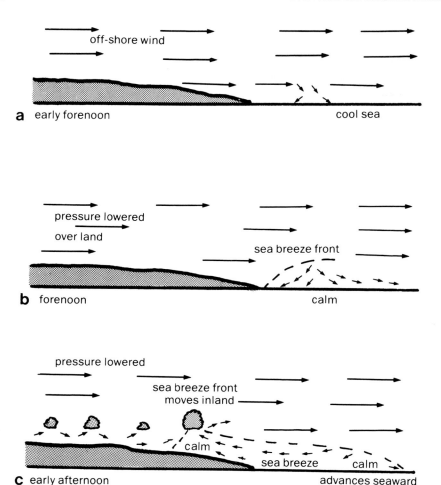

Fig. 9.1 How the seabreeze starts when the wind is off-shore

that in the evening it may well end up blowing along the coast from the right of its original direction.

Depthwise, it will be a very shallow layer hugging the sea surface when it first comes ashore, but it will deepen with time. However, its depth is measured in a few hundred feet at most. So, in a fully established breeze there is a stable deck, say, 200-400 feet deep where the wind is blowing on-shore at, for example, 8-12 knots topped by a deck where the same wind blows as in the morning sometimes in a diametrically opposite direction at a slightly higher speed (see fig. 9.2). You need to be ready for surprises if you attempt to explore the interface at the top of the breeze. You may find turbulence where the two opposing currents meet and a vector change in wind speed of as much as 25 knots between the two opposing currents.

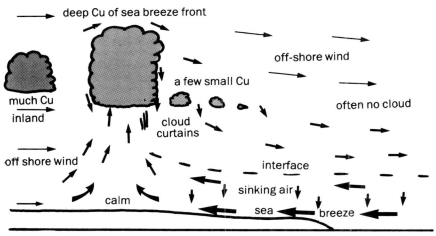

Fig. 9.2 Structure of a typical seabreeze front when it is well-established

The seabreeze inland

Once ashore, the breeze suddenly goes up a couple of gears, because convection can have its head. This convection occurs along a line called a seabreeze front where the breeze driving inland is met by the off-shore wind. The breeze usually wins this met. equivalent of arm-wrestling as it struggles to overcome the wind opposing its fight to move inland. However, you cannot have two currents of air flowing towards one another without the air going up along the line where they meet. Thus the seabreeze front is a line of stronger convection than anywhere else in the sky. By the time it has formed and is marching inland, convection has usually created fleets of Cu clouds, but along the line of the front the Cu is deeper and more active than elsewhere (see photograph 23). Thus it is normally easy to see where the seabreeze front has got to (see photograph 20), but there is another sign which helps identify its position.

Because air is ascending along the seabreeze front, it has to descend somewhere else. That descent is a slow but important part of the seabreeze's regime. It occurs over the whole of the area to seaward of the front and is often recognised by total blue sky in that direction. There may be some low-level convection in the seabreeze deck, but it is nullified by the air sinking from above it. Any Cu clouds that manage to run the gauntlet and move seaward are soon eroded out of existence. Thus any soaring on the seaward side of the seabreeze front will have to be done in mechanical (ridge) lift and so will be limited. Along the front itself care needs to be taken by hang glider and paraglider pilots, because of the strength of the convection. It is one thing for sailplane pilots to use seabreeze fronts for extended flights, but in less rigid gliders you need to be an experienced pilot to attempt the same feats. Inland from the front normal convective lift will occur just as it would on any other cumulus day.

Normally the seabreeze front moves inland with the day (see fig. 9.3). On the Sussex coast of England it normally makes some 3 knots until it meets the ridge of the South Downs. There it rests for an hour or so as it summons the strength to over-top the 700–800 feet barrier (see fig. 9.4). After that it gets a move on, making as much as 8 knots across

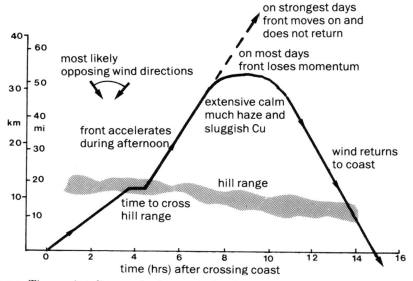

Fig. 9.3 Time against distance plot for a typical seabreeze

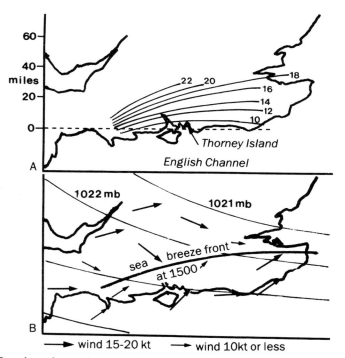

Fig. 9.4 How the seabreeze fronts usually move across south and south-east England (a), and a typical wind shift pattern in the middle of the afternoon (b)

Surrey during the afternoon. Typical times for the breeze to arrive at inland sites, having started from the coast at 1000, are shown in fig. 9.4.

As the seabreeze is a shallow wind, it will blow round high outcrops. As an example, at the Isle of Wight, which encloses the Solent, the breeze has to blow round the edges of the island because its south side rises high as 750 feet (and is generally over 400 feet) and the breeze over the sea is not often as deep as that. So, such an island or some island massif can divert the breeze and make for some odd wind directions.

While breezes are known to turn up after sunset at sites 50 miles (80km) inland, it is far more likely that you will be at the end of the seabreeze's throw if you are 30 miles (50km) or so inland. The movement of a seabreeze front that reached some 30 miles (50km) inland is shown in fig. 9.3. It had to cross a hill range and, about 8 hours after starting on the coast, it

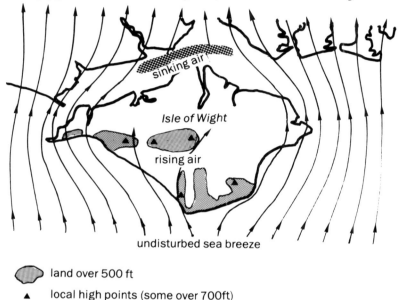

land over 500 ft

▲   local high points (some over 700ft)

Fig. 9.5 Idealised flow round the Isle of Wight. Expect the southern cliffs to be starved of air

came to a halt. Some three hours of fitful calm followed before the off-shore wind overcame the impetus of the breeze and pushed it back to the sea where it arrived around 15 hours later. Assuming the breeze started at 10 a.m., that would mean the sudden arrival of a land wind at approximately 1 a.m. This effect is academic for glider pilots who will only fly by day, but the fact that seabreeze fronts sometimes gallop inland but have to come to a halt somewhere is important.

Assessing the situation

Assume you fly a site maybe 20-30 miles (30-50km) inland from a south- or west-facing coast which is well known for generating seabreeze fronts. The morning wind blows gently from NW. Afternoon flying from a slope which faces from between north-west and north is good, but you cannot count on it extending into the evening. You have to allow for the wind faltering to little or nothing towards teatime and then changing to a direction which may be almost opposite. This new wind will be the seabreeze, but by this time it may well only make a speed of about 5 knots.

When I was serving as a forecaster at Thorney Island airbase, we did a good deal of research into seabreezes to see if their time of arrival could be forecast. We looked into this because seabreezes had a nasty habit of turning up just when aircraft were landing into what they had been told was a northerly wind only to find that as they made their final approach it had suddenly changed to a southerly seabreeze. Eventually, that did not prove to be too much of a hazard, as the power of aircraft had increased and a vector change of 20 knots was not as catastrophic as in earlier days of slower, less powerful, aircraft. However, a vector change of 20 knots when a hang glider or paraglider is coming into land could have serious consequences. On flying sites known to be within the throw of the seabreeze from the sea coast, but not too near, the breeze cannot appear very early in the day unless you are a few miles inland. For instance, you could be flying from the slopes of the hill range in fig. 9.3.

At first you are launching from the side facing the wind you had had all morning and, with considerable amounts of Cu cloud about, getting some good flights. However, for some apparently unknown reason the wind after lunch begins to drop. According to the ideas in chapter 3 concerning the diurnal variation in wind speed, the wind should still be increasing at this time. Now, being forewarned, you should recognise that a seabreeze front is probably to blame. It is the most likely reason for the wind to falter in the middle of the day.

You can therefore delay a take-off until the new breeze is established and can use the time to hike over the ridge to the coast-facing slopes to meet the new direction which will not usually be as full of lift as the morning wind was. If already airborne, and your eye tells you that you are no longer having to allow for wind in keeping along the ridge, then keep your options open and think of the consequences of having to land into a wind maybe almost opposite in direction from the one in which you took off.

Effects of the coastline

The sea is much smoother than any land surface and so the contrast between wind over the sea and over the land that it invades is very marked. Thus the coastline becomes a zone of transition between one wind regime and another – often one cloud regime and another as well.

When the seabreeze sets in around steep coasts, it becomes very much deflected by them, because it is a relatively shallow stable wind. What happens to a developed seabreeze when it blows round a high isolated island like the Isle of Wight can be seen in fig. 9.5. Here the Island deflects the streamlines which will still try to follow the waterways like the East and West Solent channels as well as Southampton Water. However, not all the south coast is high and so the air can stream in and disappear up over the Island to come down again on the opposite side of the Solent. This leaves a calm area in the lee of the island.

Similar effects must be envisaged where more or less isolated groups of hills stick up out of surrounding plains. The heights are likely to be starved of air while in their lee there may be almost no wind.

Of course, not all coastal areas are the same. For instance, where high promontories stick out into the sea, forming almost right-angled bends in the coastline, you may get two seabreeze currents set up in the morning, one coming from each of the two separate coastlines. For instance, in fig. 9.6 the Baie de la Seine is flanked by the Cotentan Peninsula

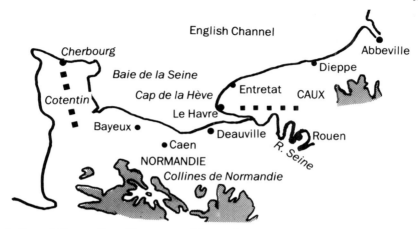

Fig. 9.6 Part of Normandie to illustrate possible sites for convergence of seabreeze currents

on the west side and by the Seine estuary and the high cliffs between Cap de la Heve and Cap d'Antifer on the east. Seabreezes can start into the mouth of the Seine, going east from the Baie while the main seabreeze is still organising itself to come in from the coast between Entretat and Dieppe. After lunchtime these two breezes will meet somewhere along the line of the Seine. This generate breezes in mid–summer. Very light general winds are required for these effects to occur because, should the wind be in the direction of one or other of these converging breezes, the one which has the wind with it will rapidly swamp the other.

Even necks of land that seem too big to produce effects like these can have their oddities. East Kent sticks out to separate the Channel from the Thames Estuary (see fig. 9.7), but the seabreeze fronts generated along the south coast between Eastbourne and Dover are very

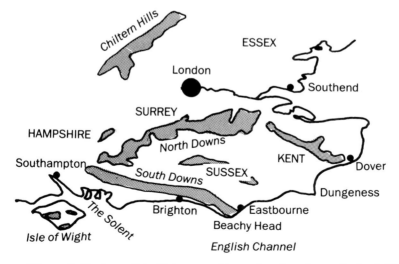

Fig. 9.7 The available slopes of the higher ground in south and south-east England. Fig. 9.3 shows that all of this area is prone to seabreeze frontal shifts

strong and may well move northwards across the whole of Kent to blow *off the land* along
the Thames Estuary coast. Anyone flying slopes of the North Downs will realise that on a
good seabreeze day they must expect the breeze eventually to come from south. Yet as the
North Downs are so close to the estuary it could well be that, on days of very light wind, a
northerly breeze sets in first in the early forenoon. It will, however, be no match for the
afternoon's breeze from the south. Something very similar occurs when the Brest Peninsula generates seabreeze fronts, as it often can do.

A similar picture is found in the extreme south-west of England, because the slopes of
Dartmoor and Bodmin Moor are not far from either the south coast of Devon and
Cornwall or the Cornish coast that starts at Land's End, finishes at Barnstaple and faces
north-west (see fig. 9.8). Both these coasts generate seabreezes and the whole promontory
that separates them is a mere 20–30 miles (32–48km) wide across Bodmin Moor, while it is
only about 45 miles (72km) from the Cornish coast to Torbay across Dartmoor. These

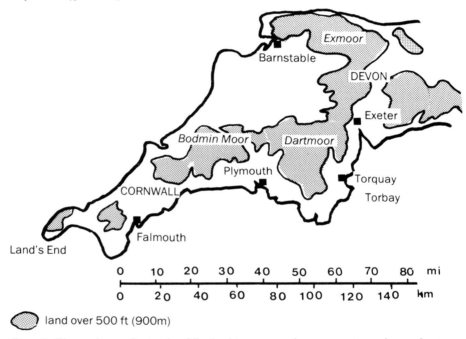

*Fig. 9.8 The south-west Peninsula of England is an area where converging seabreeze fronts
may make for some very odd wind shifts*

distances are easily spanned by seabreezes from either coastline and on light wind days
breezes will converge onto the uplands of Dartmoor and Bodmin Moor. The slopes of the
moors that look south or east will only feel the breezes from the Torbay coast or the south
coast of Devon and Cornwall, but will get a gentle NW wind. The breeze will use its help to
run in fast from the north-west Cornish coast, making for much more wind than the
forecast will have intimated.

Many more examples could be added to these, but enough has been said to illustrate the
principles. You can only decide whether such effects apply to your chosen site by looking at
the map and seeing how far you are from a coastline that may generate seabreezes. Then, if

the day dawns fair and not at all windy, you can make an informed guess as to whether or not you may have more than one wind direction to contend with during the day. Do not think that slopes in Scotland or Scandinavia that are not too far from the sea will be bereft of seabreezes. The Gulf of Bothnia, for example, has massive seabreezes, even though the summer does not get all that hot. This is because the water temperature in the Baltic is low in spring and never gets a chance to warm up fully during the short summer. So, the temperature difference between land and sea is quite large and that is what fuels the seabreeze.

TABLE 9.1 WHAT CHANCE OF A SEABREEZE?

(A) NO CHANCE IF
    (a) it is totally cloudy so that land cannot heat up
    (b) wind speed opposing the seabreeze is over 10 knots measured at about 0900 local sun time (LST)
    (c) the site is over 40 miles from main sea coast except occasionally on the best days in May and June
(B) SOME CHANCE IF
    (a) fairly thin or broken cloud (i.e. gaps in Sc cover or islands of alto clouds allowing some sunshine)
    (b) wind speed of 8-10 knots at 0900 LST but not if you are 10-20 miles inland
(C) GOOD CHANCE IF
    (a) sunny and cool before 0900 LST
    (b) wind speed less than 5-6 knots
    (c) site within 20 miles of main sea coast
For other prospects see the tables etc. below.

Making up your mind at about 0900

(A) Find the wind speed in the open as accurately as possible
(B) Which way is it blowing? (a) from land towards main sea coast; (b) from coast; (c) more or less parallel to the main sea coast.
(C) How much cloud cover is there? In effect, does the cloud stop most of the sunshine?
(D) Can you expect cumulus clouds to develop soon? That usually means mainly clear skies; a cool feel to the air (not hot or sultry).

If answer to	*And you are*	*Then a seabreeze front is possible*
(A) is 0-3 knots (B) is (a) or (c) (C) is No (D) is Yes	on coast 10 mls inland 20 mls inland 30 mls inland	any time between now and mid-morning by lunchtime by teatime unlikely but could happen in evening
(A) is 3-6 knots (B)(C)(D) as above	on coast 10 mls inland 20 mls inland 30 mls inland	late morning afternoon evening unlikely
(A) is 6-8 knots (B)(C)(D) as above	on coast 10 mls inland 20 mls inland	during afternoon late afternoon or not at all unlikely
(A) is 8-10 knots (B)(C)(D) as above	on coast 10 mls inland	late afternoon unlikely but in either case wind speed can be reduced during afternoon.
(A) is more than 10 knots (B)(C)(D) as above	on coast	Wind speed can go down in afternoon but no breeze actually develops from seaward
(B) is (b)	on coast and all inland	No seabreeze front but wind often increases markedly by afternoon. Can be very turbulent.

Notes on What Chance of a Seabreeze?
The tables are based on measurements made of seabreeze fronts on the South and East coasts of England
– specifically between Dorset and Kent on the South coast and between The Thames Estuary and
Lincolnshire on the East coast. Both these are the strongest seabreeze coasts in Britain, but the results can
apply to coastal areas of Europe between the latitudes of Denmark and the Biscay coasts of France.
Further south, seabreeze influences are stronger and breezes can set in against stronger opposing winds.

Seabreezes occur on all coasts, but on high coasts the seabreeze frontal system may not organise itself
into a continuous line a hundred or more miles long as it does over southern England. However, local
fronts occur over coasts like those of Devon and Cornwall as well as along the Brest Peninsula, the
Cotentin Peninsula etc.

In England occasional seabreezes penetrate as much as 50 miles inland – the South coast seabreeze
frontal system appearing over the Thames Valley as a late evening wind-shift. Such incursions can only
occur at the height of the season, i.e. late May and June. The tables are for more normal penetrations and
for much of the season which is from April through to September.

Seabreezes are strong in the Baltic during the relatively short summer because the waters are cold as
they are in the Adriatic due to the heat of the sun. However on the Yugoslavian side, within the compass
of the Dinaric Alps, mountain winds are prevalent over-night and are stemmed by the seabreeze force
during the day, leading to a wind minimum during the afternoon and a maximum (from the mountains)
in the morning and the evening. Similar effects can occur on the coasts of the Gulf of Lions when
seabreeze opposes the Mistral.

Because of its inherent instability, the NW wind is most likely to engender strong seabreeze fronts,
which can locally produce showers and may, when conditions are right, set off thunderstorms. Because of
this, coasts that face south through to east are more likely to exhibit seabreeze frontal effects. For example
they are less well-known on the French coast than on the English one.

How Seabreeze Fronts Move Inland
The seabreeze front starts its journey relatively slowly and maybe makes 2-3 knots in the first few hours.
It is held back by having to scale hillranges such as the South Downs and may take an hour or two to
cross them. It accelerates during the afternoon, making its highest speed between 1600 and 1800 when
the opposing wind is stabilising and decreasing. After 1800 it slows down, if indeed it has managed to
keep going for so long. How a typical front moved from the South coast of England is shown in fig. 9.4.
Afternoon and evening fliers have to contend with the re-establishment of the gradient wind. The above
facts are summarised in fig. 9.3.

OTHER LOCAL WINDS

Seabreezes, mountain and valley winds, mountain gap winds, etc. already mentioned in chapters 8 and 9 are not the only local winds the air rider may encounter. Others which are due to the updraughts and downdraughts near big cumulonimbus clouds will be looked at in the next chapter. As well as all these, however, there are, for instance:

Pseudo seabreeze fronts

These can form when one part of the terrain is in sunshine and an adjacent part is in cloud or out in fog (see fig. 10.1). Just like a seabreeze, the surface airflow is from the colder region to the warmer, and a line of converging winds forms a line of convection closely akin to a seabreeze front. The most prevalent time for these is afternoon, but they can spread cloud and/or fog to an area previously enjoying sunshine and adequate thermal lift.

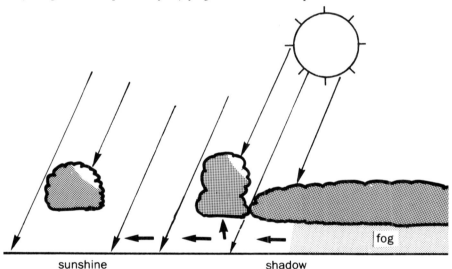

sunshine   shadow

Fig. 10.1 The 'shadow wind' is akin to a seabreeze inland

The foothills wind

There is also something which might be called a foothills wind that helps induce a sea-breeze when it blows in the early morning. What is required is slowly rising ground towards, say, downs or other hills that lie not far from the sea. The South Downs on the South Coast or the Lincolnshire Wolds on the East Coast of England during the early morning or the collines of Artois in Northern France later in the day come to mind.

Slight anabatics set in when these sun-facing slopes are warmed and there is air motion towards inland. This creates a 'vacuum' between the slopes and the coast where there is already an embryonic seabreeze system. Aided by the region just inland becoming starved of air, the seabreeze starts before one might otherwise expect it. Given more massive rising ground which faces the sun and is not far from the coast, the high ground will not allow the seabreeze to penetrate further than itself even though a foothills wind induces it to come in early. The breeze will be deflected sideways along the axis of the high ground.

The phantom beach effect

This occurs when there is warm water lying along or just off the coast. It was pointed out that the seabreeze really gets going when the tongues of the breeze pushing in towards shore arrive over warm beaches where convection can occur. If that convection can take place over warm water further out, then the breeze will blow more strongly before it ever gets to the coast (see fig. 10.2). Such warm regions occur in summer when water, warmed by the tide flooding over heated banks and mudflats, etc. in creeks, comes and lays off the

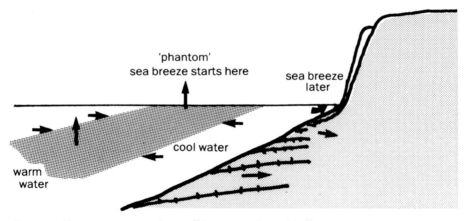

Fig. 10.2 How warmer water lying offshore can induce odd effects into the establishment of seabreezes at coastal sites

coast on the ebbing tide. It can stay there during slack water and the following early flood, and so still be there during the morning even though it was warmed by a tide that was high last evening. If there should be a 'river' of such water lying off the coast, with cooler water inshore, then air will flow from the cool inshore water to feed convection over the warm 'river', leading to late establishment of the true seabreeze.

Another complication is the undoubted fact that the time of high water affects the onset of the seabreeze. No one knows why, but that does not alter the fact that it happens, just as it is a fact that the wind comes up with the tide and goes down with it. Personal research has shown that at Thorney Island the maximum wind speed occurs within twenty minutes either side of high water. Thereafter it goes down markedly in speed.

Night winds

Night winds are only of interest to air riders when they affect the evening hours or extend their influence into the morning. In quiet weather a nocturnal wind blows from coastal hills to the sea, being at its strongest in the autumn when the land is cool but the sea is still warm from the summer. It is a mixture of katabatic wind and land breeze but, with low hills backing a coastal plain, it does not usually start until a few hours after sunset. Then it grows to a few knots during the hours after midnight and dies towards dawn or soon after (see fig. 10.3).

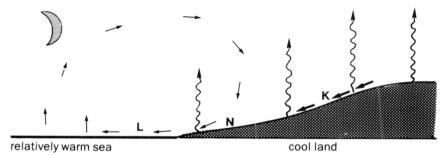

relatively warm sea   cool land

Fig. 10.3 The nocturnal wind (N) occurs near the coast where land breezes (L) are aided by katabatics (K). Inland there will only be K

However, let the coastal plain be backed by real mountains and the nocturnal wind will often blow on into the forenoon from their direction, being guided by the topography. As one approaches the Mediterranean latitudes, the regime in spring and summer (less so in autumn) is for the night wind to blow until it is stalemated by the developing seabreeze. The latter blows – often as high as 20 knots – for the day and into the evening. Then, again, stalemate occurs between the dying seabreeze and the developing night wind.

Lake plain winds

These can be very complex, due to the effect of surrounding mountains, and the only way to explain what can happen is to take an actual example (see fig. 10.4, p.100). Lakes Geneva and Neuchâtel lie on a lake plain between the Jura mountains to the west and the Savoie and Berner Alps to the east. The Jura form a wall that stretches NE-SW not far from either lake and this helps guide the local gradient winds to come from either SW or NE (occasionally N). The local winds have local names, showing how recognisable they are; when visiting a new locality it is a good idea to consult the natives about the nature of their local winds.

La vent du sud-ouest (A) comes with the southerlies ahead of depressions and this is therefore the 'bad weather' wind. As the depressions pass and the gradient winds swing in from the north, the **Bise (B)** develops, but again is guided to come from NE by the Jura. Such guided winds can grow to gale force.

The **Sechard (C)** is the valley wind that blows towards the Rhône valley through the western part of the Haut Lac and the Petit Lac as a NE wind. In settled weather the Sechard blows through the afternoon and evening but, as the settled period begins to break

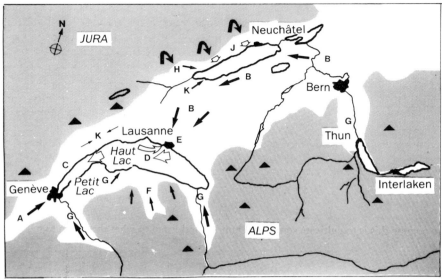

▲ Local Mountain Peak (up to 11,000 ft)

Fig. 10.4 An example of lake plain winds to illustrate that in mountainous districts there are many local winds and they get local or regional names

down, an opposing SW (gradient) wind reduces the Sechard to calm. The SW wind is called the **Vent Blanc (D)**, because it is associated with the onset of high white cirrus clouds from over the Jura.

Lake winds are not very noticeable on Lake Geneva, but as the contours slope from Geneva towards Bern so there is a tendency for a SW valley wind to blow onto the north shore of the Haut Lac around Lausanne. However, sometimes this wind will be blowing above overnight calm that exists at the surface and only the onset of convection in the morning will allow it to come down onto the surface where it reinforces the already on-shore tendency of the embryonic lake breeze. Thus an on-shore breeze suddenly develops in the early morning, sweeping away the calm.

Later, the opposing Sechard develops in opposition to the lake breeze (called **Rebat** on this shore) and stalemate produces calm. In the evening, the Rebat falters, allowing the NE Sechard to blow from the Lausanne shore. However, the katabatics from the Alps to the south blow off the opposite south shore, producing a wind called the **Chamoisine (F)**, and so oppose the Sechard which means that the centre of the lake is a region of strange wind changes during the normal quiet night. The Chamoisine may blow as strongly as 10 knots at times.

Föhn (G) arrives from the south over the Alps and can blow as strongly as Force 6 while downdraught gales result from thunderstorms coming from the directions of the Jura and the Savoie Alps. The latter produce violent and sudden gales.

Because it is close to and parallel with the Jura mountains, the Bise on Lake Neuchâtel rises to Force 8. The westerly winds of depressions come over the Jura and, falling onto the lake, can become Force 10. Guidance from the mountains usually turns such gales SW.

Le Joran (J) is the katabatic wind that sinks off the Jura. It is an unreliable wind, but when the summits are snow-capped it develops Mistral-type squalls. Another odd wind is L'Uberre (K) which gets up in the evening when the southerly gradient is strengthening. It ought to have been maximum in the afternoon following the diurnal variation in wind speed, but here the valley wind is northerly and at its maximum in the afternoon. The two oppose one another during the afternoon, but when the valley wind effect is removed in the evening the gradient wind gets its head.

Downdraught storms are sometimes very violent on Neuchâtel because of its proximity to the mountains, but Föhn does not reach there. However, very similar 'lee' winds replace it when the wind blows from over the Jura.

The small lake called the Thunersee sees the Föhn regularly and the mountain and valley wind system (page 76) works classically here. In the forenoon the mountain wind blow gently towards Bern and, after a change-over calm period, the valley wind blows towards the Bernese Alps in the afternoon as a stronger Force 2-3 W to NW wind.

Most Alpine or similar venues will have effects similar to the above and unless you have studied them for some time their antics may be something of a mystery. The only way to overcome this is to cultivate some local pundits and listen to what they have to tell you.

11

THUNDERSTORMS AND SHOWERS

From a flying point of view, thunderstorms and showers are not very different. They have to be avoided like the plague. Not only do they produce life-threateningly strong updraughts and downdraughts, but any form of rain destroys lift over wings and sudden heavy rain could spell disaster for anyone foolish enough to be caught in it.

There are days when the cumulus of morning grows upwards at alarming rates and showers then break out. The early flyer can get some good flying in, but then has to be careful not to push his or her luck as the day develops. You must monitor the early morning forecasts to see if showers are featured, but after that it is entirely up to you. No one will be able to tell you which, if any, of the showers breaking out in the local area will affect you directly or when. You have to look carefully at your own sky and remember how a showery day over land usually develops. The first Cu that appears may well look like fair-weather stuff, with very little vertical development, but then the sun will get to work on the ground. The thermals may burst through a higher inversion layer into colder air above and then there is nothing to stop the upward explosion for many thousands of feet.

Looking for showers

The signs of Cu that will grow into showers include:

(a) developing tops of some clouds around the sky so that the distance base to top (D) is greater than that from base to ground (d). It is not necessary that such 'cumulus congestus' will grow deep enough to produce showers, but they often do (see fig. 11.1).

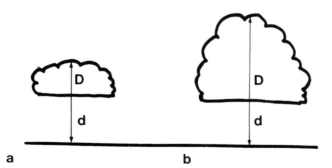

Fig. 11.1 *A rule-of-thumb method of indicating Cu clouds that are likely to grow – maybe into Cb*

(b) filmy, eyebrow-shaped, caps and skeins of 'pileus' appearing either over a growing cumulus head of left behind on the sides of one which has shot up and left the pileus cap behind (see fig. 11.2).

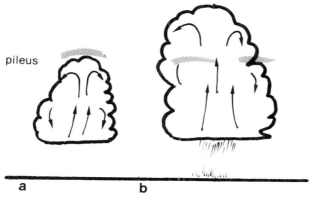

Fig. 11.2 Once the Cu is growing, look for the caps of pileus either over the tops (a) or left behind up the sides (b)

Life-cycle of showers

Any shower cloud goes through a life-cycle which typically lasts half an hour. The rain starts suddenly and heavily, and tapers off in intensity as the shower passes. Showers tend to move with the wind about half-way up their development and this may be 30 knots, even though your flying wind is only 10 knots or so. You could outdistance a shower cloud with a sailplane, but trying to fly ahead and outdistance a coming shower with a hang glider or paraglider is a dangerous and foolhardy thing to do. If you are not very close to home, then land anywhere before the monster gets you, and do not fly again until the airstream has become much more stable, which may be evening time – if then!

It is impossible for the met. office to give an adequate forecast service for showers. The radar network can see them and certain major met. facilities may be directly connected into it and have a continuous display of the present development and movement of shower belts. However, unless you can talk directly to people with access to such a facility, in real time you will have to rely on the TV met. casts to provide any view they may care to give of the recent state of the radar shower plot.

Shower belts

It is very unusual for showers to distribute themselves evenly around the day or just one part of the day – for example, afternoon. In any unstable airmass there will be airmass troughs in which showers will grow in 'belts' across the wind direction. Sometimes when showers are forecast, the morning may remain sunny, with far less cloud than the forecast ever gave you to expect. If that should happen, be very suspicious. The blue skies are probably due to subsiding air ahead of the mainly rising air in an airmass trough that is still not visible on the windward horizon. When it does come into view it will look like a coming cold front (see photograph 10), with the anvils of false cirrus cloud spreading out above a mass of lower cumuliform clouds. Expect it to last for an hour or so, after which it may well go back to blue skies again for a while as the air also subsides behind it. However, this respite cannot be expected to last, especially if, as happens in central and eastern England with NW winds, the airmass trough turns up on the hours surrounding lunch-time.

Heavy showers

These induce strong downdraught winds which spread ahead and around them and which will threaten unsecured gliders on the ground as well as saturating sails and parafoils. The performance of sailplanes can be badly affected by the buffeting they may receive on the ground in the strong gusts associated with showers. Obviously no glider with lifting surfaces still wet or even damp should take to the air after a shower. Balloons would not be up in such conditions anyway, although they might be caught by a rogue shower which appears over the obscuring edges of the wood in whose shelter they are inflating.

In hilly areas, showers can break out even though it is dry on the lowland. The upslope effect may be just sufficient to trigger Cu deep enough to develop locally into cumulo-nimbus (see photograph 11) and such Cb clouds may appear suddenly over a windward ridge to threaten an otherwise flyable domain. A more than usually keen weather eye has to be kept open in the hilly or mountainous terrains where many glider pilots are wont to fly. Of course, gliders already flying will have a better view of what is coming from windward and can warn others of the potential danger, but what if nobody is yet up?

Other forms of shower

The showers talked about above are the ones which come from deep cumulonimbus clouds that are simply overgrown Cu clouds, but the word 'showers' covers a wide range of forecast conditions when rain will occur intermittently. Sometimes older warm fronts or occlusions become showery. Then patches of rain develop and fall from an almost contin-uous layer of medium-level cloud. The darker forms of this cloud will probably preclude flying anyway, but sometimes the cloud does not look very thick and the day is quite bright – bright enough to induce the development of some patches of cumulus below the main cloudbase. In these conditions any pilot could be caught out – the weather is flyable, but it suddenly rains. The day may also be quite warm and the rain can be thundery in nature, with big spots, and in the most severe examples thunder may actually be heard – which, of course, means that lightning has occurred somewhere up there, even if it has not been seen.

When these medium-level showers occur, they induce local downdraughts which may defy all attempts to remain airborne. If it is warm, the droplets of rain may evaporate before they get to your level and so it will appear to be dry, but the downdraughts can still occur. Often the cloudbase looks quite hard, but search for any parts that appear fuzzy. It is from these fuzzy areas that the showers are occurring.

Forecasts may describe the conditions with such phrases as 'risk of outbreaks of thun-dery rain', but in domestic forecasts the old standby of 'showers' is all that may be mentioned. There is some indication of the onset of these high-level thundery conditions in the clouds which are illustrated in photograph 13. If the characteristic lines of battlements of castellanus or the sheep-like masses of floccus appear on the morning wind, then beware: firstly, of unpredictable thermal turbulences and, secondly, of the imminent outbreak of thundery showers or even thunderstorms. Again, a layer of Ac or As cloud which might not be capable of developing any showers over low ground can be induced to shower by the undulations of the air over hilly terrain. There may be large gaps in this kind of cloud cover which will have the sun shining and so producing some Cu development, but you may be surprised when one or more of these apparently innocuous cloudy islands around the sky suddenly decides to shower on you.

Thunderstorms

There are several different kinds of thunderstorm. The regime that most people call a 'thunderstorm' is often a product of an inland thermal low or a col where the summer air is sluggish and humid. Then a wide area of individual storm cells will develop into a massive storm, with buildings (and people) struck, torrential rain, and maybe hail inches deep in the roads and, in some rare cases, stones up to an inch across.

Apart from where it first develops, this form of summer thunderstorm moves very slowly and can be heard coming from as much as 10 miles (16km) away. However, the visibility on such thundery days is often poor – it may amount almost to fog limits near the coast – and so it may not be possible to see the developing thunder-heads until they begin to produce precipitation, soon followed by thunder and lightning. The most likely time for such outbreaks is afternoon and evening, sometimes going on into the night, but this is not a hard and fast rule. How such storms are built and maintained from storm cells is covered in 'Thunderstorms' pages 175-77, but it is worth mentioning here that storm areas can develop across the wind direction that is driving them. You have to be careful if you wish to know which way the storms are heading.

Thunderstorms move with the wind which is roughly half-way up their development. That means roughly the same height as Ac and As clouds exist. If you suspect that thunderstorms are a possibility, try to follow the motion of any alto clouds there may be about – that will be the way the storms will move. You cannot rely on the surface wind to tell you anything about the motion of nearby storms, because for one thing it is often light and variable and subject to being steered by the surrounding terrain, and, for another, big storms generate their own surface winds. The bad storm comes up against the wind, but the wind is one of the storm's own making as it sucks in air to feed its developing updraughts.

This pre-storm wind may be 10 knots or so, but you have to allow for this changing to a big gust of as much as 40 knots from the direction of the storm just ahead of the dark roll-cloud that marks the forward edge of the thunderclouds. Sailplanes must be fully tethered (if they cannot be put into shelter) and you must anticipate damage from hail-stones. Hang gliders must be fully unrigged and stowed unless, of course, you are caught out, at which stage the remarks given for sailplanes apply. Paragliders should be in the bag or rucsac long before a storm strikes, because the merest sound of thunder ought to send those who are flying back to the ground immediately. It is a terrifying thought that the unwary might conceivably be caught in a storm's updraught which can ascend at as much as 50 knots. Whirled up to dizzy heights would mean almost certain death from exposure and lack of oxygen. The other alternative is just as deadly – being savagely forced into the ground by the downdraughts. These remarks also apply to big shower clouds which do not produce thunder.

The light winds that characterise the mornings of days when storms are going to break out and the general fairness of such days may tempt balloonists into the air. However, the balloon is at great risk from Cb updraughts and downdraughts, because there is absolutely nothing the pilot can do and, again, if there is any sign of storms the balloon should be landed as soon as possible and rapidly deflated before there is any chance of the big storm winds getting hold of it. In this context it is important to realise that the 'nose' of the strong cold wind that precedes the storm may be spread some way ahead of it and would constitute a grave hazard to any balloon or glider caught in it.

Here are some actual measurements of wind direction and speed, plus temperature, as a big storm approached. This storm came up against the wind until the nose of cold air, spreading forwards ahead of the storm, reversed the direction by 180°. At the same time, the temperature began to fall.

Storm travelling on a westerly 20kt wind

Miles (km) from nose of cold air	4(6.5)	3(5)	2(3)	1(1.5)	0	1(1.5)	2(3)	3(5)	4(6.5)	5(8)	6(9.5)
Time (minutes)	0	3	6	9	12	15	18	21	24	27	30
Wind direction	NE	L/V	SW	L/V	SW	SW	SW	SW	SW	SW	SW
Speed (knot)	10		15		30	42	40	10	35	20	20
Temp. (deg. F)	82	82	81	81	80	78	76	75	74	74	73

(L/V = light/variable)

The hang glider and paraglider pilots who frequent the high places must remember that thunderstorms can approach behind ridges and can only be detected when they suddenly rear into view above the flying site. The pre-storm wind will blow up slopes that look away from the coming storm and, if the origin of this wind is not understood, it can seem a heaven-sent opportunity to get into the air. The result could be disastrous, not necessarily from the storm as such but from the downdraught gale that will cascade down the slopes – a vast, invisible avalanche of cold, crushing wind in which nothing can fly (see fig. 11.3).

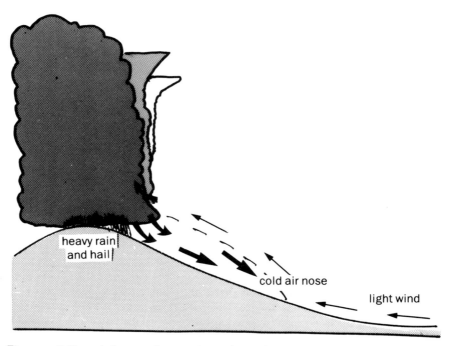

heavy rain and hail

cold air nose

light wind

Fig. 11.3 Falling winds are a threat on lower slopes when storms occur higher up

It is important to be aware of downdraught gales, because even though a flying slope is of the order of 20 or more miles (30km) from the major ridge it is possible for the falling winds to reach you without you being aware that there is a storm in progress. Often thunder does not carry further than 10 miles (16km) and in daylight lightning is unlikely to be seen either. At 40 knots a falling wind will only take a quarter of an hour to cover 10 miles (16km). These may be extreme values, but they indicate just one more hazard of weather in the mountains which must be borne in mind when you are prospecting a site for flying that lies under the aegis of a mountain ridge. We must take our cue from the experiences of sailors who frequent lakes in the Alpine Foreland. Sirens sound for them when there is a risk of sudden strong winds, because lake sailors know how sudden and prodigious are the gales that spring up from nowhere in the narrow valleys that look up towards the mountains. No one dissembles – they just clear the water as fast as possible. Those paraglider pilots who have hiked a long way up hill to an almost perfect site are most prone to risk, taking off in marginal conditions so as not to waste all that effort. They are the ones who most need to stop and think about the possible hazards – but there will be no siren warning them of what is about to strike out of the blue!

Thunderstorms can break out on fronts. On cold fronts they are part and parcel of the dynamics of the front and will be embedded in the frontal cloud. With active, fast-moving fronts they will usually pass relatively quickly. The whole affair may not last more than half an hour to an hour. However, when cold fronts (or occlusions) become slow-moving over land, an almost continuous line of storms may develop along the line of the front. Such storms are a risk to all aviation and will certainly be mentioned on Volmet, etc.

More prevalent in north-west Europe are thundery troughs. A particular form of these develops over central France on warm summer days and moves up into the Low Countries and across the English Channel and into southern England. Before the incursion of such troughs (which tend to come in the afternoon) the mornings are usually but not necessarily hot and the winds are normally light to moderate. The visibility may well be poor and the sky populated with castellanus and floccus moving up on medium-level winds from the direction in which the storms will eventually come. Over southern England these winds are often from the south, while the surface wind is easterly, but elsewhere things could well be different.

Such thundery outbreaks produce very pronounced thunder and much 'sheet' lightning as well as ground strikes. They are usually not as severe as thunderstorms that develop in thermal or other shallow lows (described at the beginning of this chapter).

Safety in storms

High places will be closer to the cloud base than the lowlands will and the intensity of the electrical phenomena may be very frightening. If caught on a mountain, it is important to select a shelter which will not make you the target for the effects of lightning strikes that may be occurring higher up.

It is an unfortunate fact that to be safe from lightning strikes and the passage of electric currents down the mountain slopes from strikes higher up (earth currents) you have to sit out in the downpour and brave the hailstones. Pinnacles of any kind are dangerous in storms, but flying slopes are relatively safe. However, the first reaction when it starts to rain is to seek shelter against a boulder or cliff edge or in an overhang or gulley. These are the worst places to be. Earth currents will take the shortest route down a mountain side and will jump across gaps using people sheltering there as handy conductors (see fig. 11.4). Mountaineers have discovered that the safest place near a cliff-edge is to be at least a yard from the base of the cliff and the latter must be over 30ft (10m) high. You should sit in the position shown, even though you will be tempted to occupy the overhang. There is a simple way to find the safe zone by mentally drawing a 45° line from the top of the sheltering rock-face

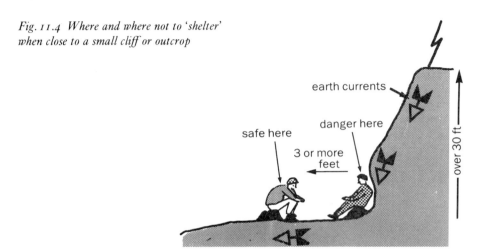

Fig. 11.4 Where and where not to 'shelter'
when close to a small cliff or outcrop

and getting over 15 yards (13.5m) away from the base (see fig. 11.5). Further out than this is considered best – somewhere between 50 and 150 yards (50 and 140m) – if the cliff is high enough. Isolated boulders and isolated trees are very dangerous places by or under which to shelter, but as they tend to 'attract' lightning so they can be used as safe havens by squatting out several yards away from them. Any metal objects must be removed well away from sheltering people.

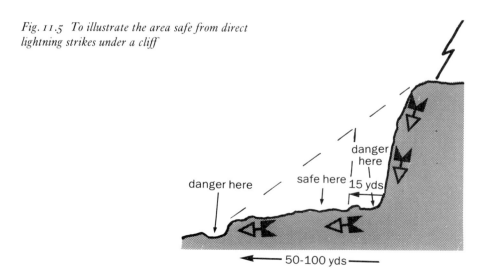

Fig. 11.5 To illustrate the area safe from direct
lightning strikes under a cliff

The higher you are, the more terrifying an electric storm. Cairns on mountain tops are often blasted asunder by the repeated strikes of lightning – not necessarily from the same storm – upon them, and the rocks become covered by 'lightning glaze' where the intense heat generated has melted the surfaces and vitrified them.

It is possible that some paraglider pilots will hike their gliders to very high and otherwise inaccessible places in order to enjoy long flights. Never make such expeditions alone and make doubly sure that there are no risks inherent in the weather forecasts. Members of such expeditions should carry between them the necessary 'iron rations' and weatherproofs that will ensure that they have the means to sit out a sudden unexpected clamp of fog until the weather clears. As the 'fog' is most likely to be cloud, it can last for many hours and, in some cases, for days. Resist the temptation to slog it back through the murk unless the way is particularly well marked. The moment you realise you are lost, seek the nearest shelter and stay there, wrapped up in your wing if need be. You will, of course, have told someone when and where you expected to get to: it makes it easier for rescue teams to find you if you are not too far from your chosen route.

12

BARRIERS TO THE WIND

The air within the boundary layer is always going to be mixed up by the effects of turbulence and, as seen in chapter 6, turbulence occurs on two main scales. These are:

(a) mechanical turbulence – due to the air colliding with obstacles such as trees, buildings, quarries, etc.

(b) thermal turbulence – due to the effects of thermal currents. This is on a much grander scale than mechanical turbulence.

Mechanical turbulence will be most apparent near the ground and so particularly affects take-offs and landings, while thermal turbulence will be felt throughout the flying layer. This chapter is mainly about the effects of mechanical turbulence.

At low wind speeds (around 5 knots or less) airflow tends to be laminar and to blow in streamlines, but as the wind speed increases so larger and larger turbulent eddies are formed, and any pretentions to laminar flow disappear.

The typical time period of the wind shifts induced by mechanical turbulence is in the order of seconds, while that of thermals, in minutes. All pilots need to know about the effects of obstructions when they take-off or land in their lee, and research has shown that the sheltering effects of trees can be divided by the amount of frontage they cover, as follows:

(1) Open barriers – providing less than 40% cover, with considerable gaps in the tree line (see fig. 12.1).

(2) Medium-dense barriers – providing 40-80% cover, with more trees than gaps.

(3) Dense barriers – providing more than 80% cover, with very few, if any, gaps.

The effects of a typical dense barrier are felt, for example, in the lee of a thick wood. Here the wind speed does what one would expect. It is zero close up to the trees and then rises more or less gradually as the distance from the trees increases. As seen in fig. 12.2, the only practical way to assess the effects is by measuring your distance in barrier heights (h). Thus when you are ten barrier heights (10h) from the edge of the wood you will have about half the undisturbed wind speed and will need to move out to some 30h before the wind is unaffected by the barrier. The shape of the wood, however, makes some difference and the more aerodynamic the profile of the wood the closer will the wind return to normal. The wind also slows down as the wood becomes shorter in the direction of the wind.

The really interesting cases occur with open and medium–dense barriers. Here, the least wind speed is not up close to the trees but some 5h from them. It is easy to monitor this distance by using the outstretched hand at arm's length, as shown in fig. 12.3. The reason for what may seem a rather surprising result is that in the lee of a solid or dense barrier the wind speed only increases from above as the wind descends and there is a back eddy trying to fill the partial vacuum in direct lee of the obstruction. However, when some of the wind can also filter through the barrier itself it opposes the back eddy near the ground and this opposition makes itself felt most strongly at about 5h.

To be sure of feeling most of the wind speed you need to be over 20h from dense and open barriers, but at 20h you will still only have some 60% of the full wind speed when the barrier is medium-dense. The wind also begins to be affected when you are about 9h on the

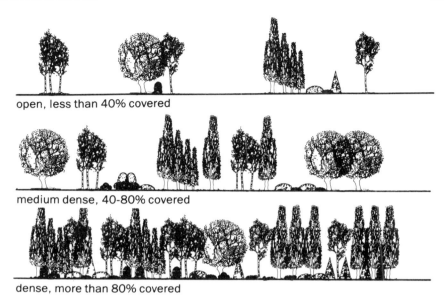

open, less than 40% covered

medium dense, 40-80% covered

dense, more than 80% covered

Fig. 12.1 To illustrate the usually accepted divisions of barrier density which affect the wind in lee

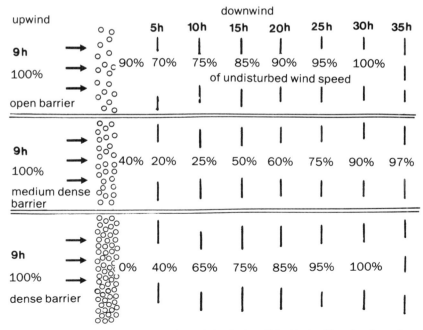

Fig. 12.2 The actual percentage wind speeds in the lee of the kinds of barrier shown in fig. 12.1

windward side of a barrier and here it does not matter what kind of barrier is involved. Again, you can monitor this 9h by turning your open hand round and fitting the barrier height to the distance between your fourth and little fingers (see fig. 12.2).

It will often happen that a barrier comes to an end near you and then how does the wind blow round the ends? Also, what happens when the wind is not blowing directly over the barrier? Some idea has been gained from research done with medium–dense barriers (see fig. 12.4). What this shows is that there is a lobe of enhanced wind speed off the end of the barrier exposed to the wind, but that the lowest wind speed is to be found near the lee end.

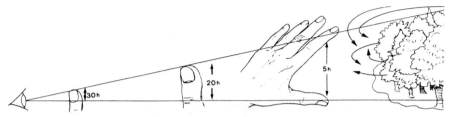

Fig. 12.3 How to use your hand as a measure of distance from a barrier. Balloonists will find the 5h yardstick very useful

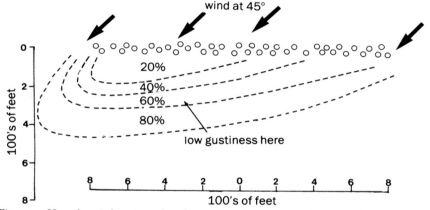

Fig. 12.4 How the wind varies in lee of a medium–dense barrier when the wind is at an angle to the barrier

This minimum speed tends to occur about half as far out as when the wind is blowing directly over the barrier. As the wind becomes even more parallel to the barrier, it tends to develop more gustiness.

Possible effects

Paragliders: if forced to land into a space sheltered by a barrier, expect to have to use stronger flare as the wind speed opposing your forward motion rapidly drops. Do not fly motorised paragliders into such shelter unless it is quite unavoidable; if you have to, then use plenty of power and do not cut it until you are fully on the ground.

Hang gliders: in windy conditions it may seem advantageous to fly into the sheltering effect of the trees so that the sail will be more manageable when you have landed. However, if you get anywhere near 5h and the wind is coming straight over the barrier you may have to fly so much faster on the last few feet of the approach that it would have been less dangerous to land clear of the shelter. Again, motorised hang gliders, having more freedom of action, can usually avoid landing into the maximum effects of shelter. Use your thumbnail size as a yardstick to judge when you are entering the sheltered zone below 30h.

12.1 Balloonists will seek shelter in the lee of a barrier, but must beware of the effects of rising into the wind over the top

Balloons: the advantages of rigging and inflating in the zone of maximum shelter are obvious, but you have to allow for the wind being *five times* stronger above the tree tops when the barrier is medium–dense and two and a half times stronger in the lee of a dense barrier. As a balloon rises, so that only the upper part is in the unobstructed wind, partial deflation will occur. This is partly overcome by the rounded top giving aerodynamic lift, but with a little more elevation the flame will be deflected, so reducing the lift. Very quickly the rising balloon will gain the same speed as the wind and so the positive effect of aerodynamic lift will be lost. The combination of the negative lift factors means that there must be plenty of excess lift available on take-off in the lee of a barrier.

Sailplanes: should only have to land close to barriers in an emergency, but the approach must be from as far away as possible or the rapid drop in opposing wind speed could induce the risk of coming to grief in the trees.

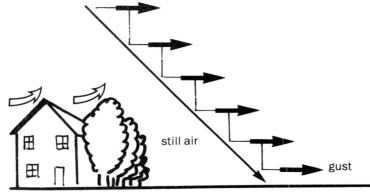

still air

gust

Fig. 12.5 The 'escalator' analogy to show how the gusts suddenly appear in the lee of dense barriers

13

FOG AND VISIBILITY

In the kinds of conditions when most gliders will fly there is very little chance of fog, and visibility should not be a problem either. Having said that, it is important to understand the conditions under which fog is likely to form, and what factors control how far you can see.

Types of fog

There are four main ways in which fog is formed.

(1) *Radiation fog* – forms overnight and normally disperses with the day.

(2) *Advection fog* – is already in existence and is transported to your site by the wind.

(3) *Orographic* or *upslope fog* – is cloud on the slopes and over the tops of high ground.

(4) *Sea fog* – may be advection fog when it rolls in on the back of the wind. Those who fly coastal cliffs should keep a weather eye seaward for the rogue fog bank that can be brought in by a developing seabreeze.

Radiation fog will often be an accompaniment to the kind of weather regime which will make for good flying later in the day. This is because it requires clear skies overnight which are characteristic of maritime Polar airmasses over land. The mP airmass will generate Cu clouds by day, as it readily engenders thermals. The maritime Tropical airmass is prone to fog, as it is often very moist and any warm-wet wind from the SW or nearby quadrants should be treated with caution.

Valley fog

The glider pilot may well find the valleys filled with radiation fog on his way up to higher ground to seek the good flying conditions expected later in the day. If, when driving up, you break out into sunshine you will see the fog laid like a mass of white candyfloss in the valleys below and, when shallow, the incongruous sight of church steeples, factory chimneys, etc. poking through the fog top. The sunshine will disperse that fog, but it can often produce a fumey unformed kind of cumulus as it does so (see photograph 13.1).

If there should be a cloud layer above the fog – which can happen when a previously clear night has been invaded by a layer of stratocumulus or altocumulus/altostratus – it will be slow to clear and may indeed linger all day in the winter half of the year.

Clearance

The strength of the sun is usually enough to clear radiation fog in summer despite overlying cloud sheets. However, fog is the most notoriously difficult weather phenomenon to forecast, both in its formation and in its clearance, and you cannot rely too heavily on the official forecasts. So, here are some ways in which radiation fog can be cleared.

13.1   This shows typical valley fog on a quiet, cool morning

(1) The arrival of dryer air from higher up when a katabatic wind develops.

(2) The arrival of a cloud layer. This is contrary to what has been said above about cloud making fog persist, but either event may happen depending on the conditions. An influx of cloud in the early night may well prevent fog forming in the first place.

(3) The formation of hoar frost. If the moisture is trapped as ice on the grass, etc., it cannot participate in the formation of fog. This is the basis of a saying we had when I was a forecaster, 'If we frost we don't fog, and if we fog we don't frost!' Neither of these may be universally true, but they are a guide. Thin, shallow fog in the early stages of formation is transparent to radiation from the ground and so may not blanket the loss of heat as thicker fog or a cloud layer may do.

(4) Wind at the top of the fog layer can advect the fog and can lift it up the slopes so that it clears at low level and makes higher ground, previously free, fog-bound. This may well occur when the first increasing wind comes ahead of an encroaching depression.

(5) You can just drive or walk out of a local fog bank into clearer conditions. If you do, it is best not to believe that all is now well, as you may soon enter another patch.

Fog and wind speed

Fog forms most readily when there is some wind. If there is flat calm, the fog often forms in sheets and wraithes near the ground. What is required is for the moisture-laden air near the surface to be slightly mixed by turbulence with the air above it. However, local shelter may make it look as if there is no wind where you are. For some 60% of foggy hours the wind at 30ft (10m) is between calm and 2 knots, and for a further 30%, between 3 and 5 knots. Above 8 knots almost all fogs clear, although there is a situation where radiation fog and advection fog may mingle and maintain fog conditions even with winds as high as Force 4. A prime example is the North Sea 'haar' which is a form of advection fog when light to moderate winds blow from NE on the east coast of Britain.

Fog and the weather map

Low wind speeds which favour fog go with areas of slack isobars on the weather map. That means that fog is far more likely in anticyclonic conditions than in others. However, wind direction also plays a part and in Atlantic Europe the moistest air usually comes on south-westerly winds while dry air comes off Continental Europe and often on SE winds. North-westerlies tend to dry out as they traverse the high ground of western Britain, but while the NE wind may be dry on the Continent it may well become fog-laden after traversing the North Sea. In fig. 13.1 a typical ridge of high pressure is shown sprawled over a land mass. On the edges of the ridge the wind is too strong for fog, so this is a low risk

Fig. 13.1 A ridge of high pressure sprawls across an area from the south-west. Where is the greatest fog risk? And where is there none?

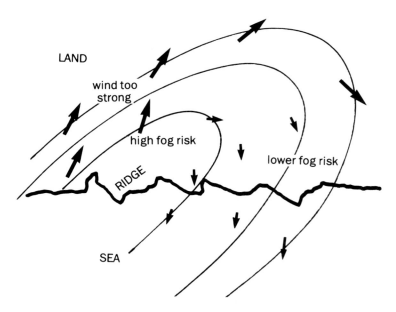

area. The area of highest risk is where the wind comes from warmer southern seas and the gradient is slack. After the air has travelled a long way over land, it will have lost much of its moisture and so the fog risk will be much lower, despite the isobars being well spaced.

Visibility

The official limits for fog, mist, etc. are given in Part 2; from a practical point of view they are only a guide for the glider pilot. If you are forecasting for big jets which can only land on fully equipped airfields, then there are stringent limits on the available landing places. With paragliders and hang gliders, if it looks as though the visibility is deteriorating badly, there are many places where you can make a rapid emergency landing, so the incidence of fog is not such a hazard as with other forms of aircraft. The factors which affect visibility include:

(1) the relative humidity of the air
(2) the wind speed
(3) the particulates, like smoke and dust, in the air
(4) the degree of stability
(5) the form of precipitation, i.e. drizzle, rain, snow, etc.

Good or exceptional visibility is to be found under the first cirrus of a coming warm front. This is due to dry, clean air sinking below the encroaching frontal surface. It is a well-known sign of coming trouble. If, when flying a high site, the mountains or the distant hills seem to be much closer and clear-cut than before, take it as a sign that you should soon consider packing up and going home.

Visibility will normally be good on good flying days, because the mixing that is produced by convection will spread whatever meteors there are through a considerable depth of the atmosphere. Note that the word 'meteors' as used here means any particles, such as water vapour, ice crystals, dust, smoke, sea salt (from breaking waves) and various chemicals from factory chimneys, etc. If the particles are water-based, they are called hydrometeors.

Once the air begins to stabilise with the onset of evening, the visibility is bound to drop and it drops most rapidly just around sunset when the air is cooling at its maximum rate. It may look then as if it will be a misty night and you will often be surprised at the sharp way the lights twinkle after dark, showing that the visibility has improved. The early morning is also a time of stability when whatever murk may have been generated locally overnight is trapped below the inversion and so even if there is no mist or fog the visibility is often quite poor at this time of day. Visibility improves the moment convection can start and so good flying weather and good visibility tend to go hand in hand.

How the fog distributes itself throughout the day and the year at Liverpool Airport is shown in fig. 13.2, p.118. There is a fog risk during the year around sunrise, but only in the winter is there the same risk later in the day. This kind of diagram could be drawn for most low-lying areas and the results of its data are particularly true for most airfields.

For any locality, specific wind directions will affect visibility if there are sources of smoke, etc. in them. These smoke sources need not be very near. For example, the east coast of England can have much reduced visibility in the afternoons, due to industrial smoke from Belgium and northern France. You have to remember people's habits. Factories and homes start to emit smoke around eight or nine in the morning and then the wind has to be given time to carry that to you. When the wind is from the direction of an industrial heartland, such as the Ruhr in Germany, expect the visibility to drop as the day progresses, depending on how far you are from the source of pollution.

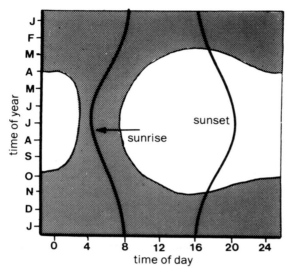

Fig. 13.2 How fog distributes
itself by time of year and time
of day at Liverpool airport.
Any similar inland place close
to a river and reasonably low-
lying will show a similar
pattern. We see that in summer
fog affects only the dawn
period, whereas in winter fog
can occur at any time of day

Visibility and fronts

It is as well to remember from a travelling point of view (you should not be flying in these conditions) that the onset of a warm front of occlusion will generate upslope fog and will do so well before your lowland experience might lead you to expect any trouble.

Rain from fronts, providing it is not heavy, does not greatly reduce visibility. However, drizzle does and on windward slopes the chance of continuous drizzle is high. Combined with upslope fog, drizzle can reduce visibility to less than 50 yards (45.5m).

Once the front has passed, the fog risk remains, or even increases in the warm air, and will be there for as long as the warm sector takes to pass. Sometimes fronts become slow moving and then fog can persist for hours (or even days in the worst cases). Apart from the loss of visibility during the heavy rain at the head of ana cold fronts, the cold front (or the cold front part of occlusions) should not greatly affect visibility. Having said this, if you are going to fly in spring or late autumn, you should allow for the precipitation from fronts being snow and, of course, there is nothing like snow for suddenly obliterating everything that was familiar around you. The higher you go, the greater chance there is that fronts will bring you snow and that they will do so suddenly and occasionally out of the blue. The forecast may say 'snow showers', but often there is next to no break between the end of one shower and the arrival of the next, so that the 'showers' seem to be continuous snow – which is often heavy.

Once you have lying snow, an increasing wind can have that snow drifting, again cutting visibility where it is blowing and causing drifts, etc. When warmer winds come in over thawing snowfields, then visibility will often be down to mist or even fog limits.

Seabreeze fronts produce a change of visibility which, while it is not at all dangerous, can be quite useful. The air off the sea is, in general, clean while that over the land is less so. Therefore, the seabreeze front can often be seen as the division bewteen clear and less clear air which helps the flyer to check its progress. The glider pilot needs to stay on the landward (dirty) side of the front.

14
ASSESSING THE SITUATION

Throughout this book there is advice about how to forecast what is likely to happen to the weather in the short term. There is, however, no substitute for the established weather forecasting services. They do not spend vast quantities of money on fast computers and peripherals without being able to see the trends better than we can. So, it is important to base your thoughts about whether flying is in or out on their predictions. It is only at the end of the day when you are close to the time when you wish to fly or are actually on site that you will be able to do better than the professionals, and then only in your own local area.

Here are some prompts as to what to do and think about in the days before you hope to fly. No set of suggestions, however detailed, could suggest all the wrinkles there may be in the situation, but perhaps a hint here and there will aid you in seeking out information you want. You may wish to go abroad to experience conditions that you cannot expect to get in your own country and will then be looking at, or listening to, foreign forecasts. That may tax your knowledge of the language and so make you more dependent on your own ideas, with a bit of help from locals who speak your tongue.

As with many things meteorological, there is often no simple answer and, when it comes to precise localities and times, no answer at all. However, the following notes may help.

Up to five days in advance

Most countries use the routine six-day forecasts to screen the trends for the coming five days or so. Find out when these are, so that you can get an idea of whether there is any point in even thinking about flying, say, at the weekend when it may only be Tuesday. In farming areas there may be a Sunday screening of weather trends for the coming week. This will usually come out on the local TV service around the middle of the day, because at that time most farmers can watch it. The five-day forecast is also to be found on the telephone, but just check the cost before you use this facility too much. In Britain the National Five-day Forecast is on 0898 500 430.

As the time period shortens, you can believe the forecast more and more. There are situations in which anticyclones are fixed *near* you when you can expect the weather and wind at the end of the period to be fairly right, but not when the high centre is *over* you! When a succession of lows is crossing the country, there is no way the forecasters can get the position of the lows exactly right five days, or even three days, in advance. You can expect frontal positions to be even more subject to errors of many hundreds of miles. I do not say it does not happen – it is just that you cannot rely on it.

There only need be a low centre near your site on the forecast chart and the probability of the winds being right in direction and speed is very low. One of the more believable situations is when there is a high stuck to one side of the venue and lows, on the other, and you lie under the isobars that stream between them. That often means the wind direction will remain much the same over a period of days ahead. In any case, your own experience will soon prove that some situations and long-range forecasts are more reliable than others.

The day before

Now you can begin to believe the forecasts in detail and can plan accordingly. However, even here you have to be careful. Research done on fronts during the period November 1983 to February 1984 (Meteorological Office Annual Report 1984) shows that fronts are quite often forecast as being ahead of where they actually turn up. The situation is worst for cold fronts which are prone to developing waves that slow them up. Forecasters are better with warm fronts and occlusions, but even so these still normally turn up later than predicted. To put it in perspective, two thirds of the fronts were forecast within two hours of the actual time they arrived, but a few were as much as 6 to 8 hours adrift. Very few turned up sooner than expected – which is a good trait. In this context read about waves in Part 2 so that when you are actually on site and looking for the cloud of a cold front or occlusion to clear you can get a better idea of when the clearance will come.

The charts screened during the evening telecasts are all based on the same computer-aided forecasts done by the big regional stations such as Bracknell in Britain, Paris in France, Offenbach in Germany. It does not matter whether you see a national forecast or a local one; the forecasters will all have done their presentations on the same faxed forecast charts and with the same advice from above. The local forecaster will be able to refine the information with his knowledge of the local area, but usually the chart symbols used cover hundreds of square miles/kilometres, and so there is no pretence at precision.

Forecasters would obviously like to improve their forecasts. They could be more accurate given the time and if released from the constraints put on them by the media. They get it right most often with aircrew, because they are in direct contact with them and the recipients have a firm grounding in met. The media presenters do a good job, in view of how hemmed in they are by sparsely-timed slots and the injunction that they must not 'bore the viewer'.

For more precision you can go to the telephone service. In Britain, for example, there is a 'glider's' forecast under the title of 'Metplan' which is done for light aviation up to 2000ft. This will figure amongst the best services you can monitor.

The aviation weather service is Volmet plain language forecasts and actual met. reports from a mixed clutch of stations. For these you have to have the necessary VHF receiver with sideband facility.

The overnight forecasts get the wind directions right most of the time – except, again, when you are close to the centres of pressure systems. However, only your knowledge of the site you hope to fly can refine the directions and speeds given. Factors such as seabreezes may not be mentioned on many days when they will occur or when they will modify the winds near the coast. Forecasters mention seabreezes for some coasts and forget others where breezes will still occur. When seabreezes are mentioned for coasts other than the one where you may be flying, it is best to assume that you could get seabreeze effects, too, and to keep an eye out for them.

Wind direction will help in assessing the prospects of thermic flight. The wind from the quadrants round NW is much more likely to produce thermic conditions than a wind from similar quadrants round SW. However, when winds are routed round local, relatively small, pressure centres, then unstable conditions can come in from unusual directions such as S or SE. A case in point is when a cool showery airstream comes in from a southerly point. Nine times out of ten you will find, when you look at the weather map, that there is a low not far away to the west.

The morning

This is the time when you have to come to grips with things as they really are and can have some confidence in how they may turn out. Morning telecasts can be a real help, because they will often show how the cloudy areas are moving through a sequence of Meteosat images. You can then see if it is likely that cloud you have now will clear, or whether the clear morning is going to be invaded by cloud extensive enough to rub out any convection that may develop.

Frontal positions will be much more reliable and you will get some advice about how they are moving to help you decide whether to go early before the frontal cloud arises or later when it has passed. However, remember the remarks about the timing of fronts.

Having an idea about the weather and the wind direction, it is time to think about local conditions. Have you studied the contours of your site and maybe drawn a few tentative streamlines so you can more confidently predict the likely wind direction and so go to the right slope?

Are the winds and weather conducive to seabreezes and are you within their throw?

Are there likely to be any overnight katabatics or mountain winds still blowing? Or, later in the day, will there be valley winds reversing the morning trends?

Have you considered valley fog which might impede your progress up to higher ground? Or is there any risk that upslope fog may be over the site or perhaps invade it later?

At coastal sites what chance is there of a sudden clamp of sea fog? The local coastguard is the best bet here, but remember the chance that a seabreeze will bring in an offshore fog-bank in the middle of the day.

Now for some other possible hazards.

If the forecast should mention the possibility of showers, it may not make the whole day unflyable. Early mornings up to 'elevenses' may well be very good, but you may have to abandon the lunch-time and afternoon periods. However, a major hazard of going to elevated sites is that the fine clear morning with excellent visibility is the one which is most likely to become a deluge of showers by the afternoon. You could come back to good flying later afternoon or early evening, especially if the slope faces the sun.

If there is a warm front or occlusion moving your way, remember that the cirrostratus veil will extend hundreds of miles ahead of where the front is on the ground and will effectively kill convection, even if the cirrus ahead of it does not. This is also the situation where the W wind backs S and increases with time.

If a warm front is confidently expected to move through during the day, there could be a flyable slot behind it. However, air in the rear of warm fronts is often stable and there is much cloud about. It could be low cloud with drizzle, but that depends on how wet the air is in the rear of the front. You may be able to get some ideas about that from the forecasts. It is important to realise that the forecast may not mention upslope fog in the rush to get the main points over.

If the coming front is a cold front, what kind of a front is it? Does the forecast indicate a full-blown ana front or just the whisper of a kata front, or, more likely, something in between? What intelligence can you get about the air behind it? Do they go for showers on a grand scale? Or showers here and there which a lot of people will miss altogether? If the latter, you could get some good flying behind the cold front.

Using the ideas given under Geostrophic wind in Part 2 you can see what the forecast expects in the way of gradient wind speed (which can be taken as the flying speed to prevent you going up in dangerously high winds). You may be able to assess it by eye when there is not much doubt that the wind speed is 10 knots or less. To be more sure, why not video the chart and then freeze the image on the screen so that you can study it? You often only need a rough estimate. You can then see if stronger winds are likely to set in behind coming fronts later in the day. Or maybe a comparison of actual and forecast charts will show that the gradient is tightening during the day and you can allow accordingly. It is very little use relying on the wind speeds given on TV charts, as terrain is not taken into consideration.

If you get some actuals from a met. station not far from you, it is not at all certain that the winds will be the same where you are. You only have to look at fig. 8.5 to realise that. Only over a coastal plain close to the sea can the wind that is forecast be the one that really affects the site.

If, for example, you get up early to hear the actual reports from coastal stations at the end of the 0555 Shipping Forecast (1515m, 198kHz), you have to remember that they are chosen to be representative of conditions over the sea. If the wind direction is from seaward, they represent the sea only and the wind ashore must be reduced accordingly. If the wind is off the land, then they are representative of the land – but only the land close to the sea! Obviously 'deep-sea' stations, such as Channel Light Vessel, will only be representative of the sea, whatever the wind direction.

In all this, do not forget local radio. Their forecasts often take account of local conditions better than any other medium. It goes without saying that you should not make any life and death decisions on the chat of disc-jockeys, who often misinterpret what they are given anyway.

There are many other situations which have not been covered here, but maybe enough has been said to prompt you to seek good advice before you commit yourself to the restless air.

Part 2

TERMS AND EXPLANATIONS
IN ALPHABETICAL ORDER

Flying is a technical sport. In the first part of this book, for ease of understanding lengthy explanations have been avoided wherever possible and often definitions of terms and phrases have not been given. Part 2, however, provides more details and definitions to explain and expand points mentioned in the previous chapters. It also bears in mind the needs of those studying for proficiency tests.

ADIABATIC A term which you will meet in relation to the rate at which the air temperature lapses in a parcel of rising air. It means 'without gain or loss of heat' and in any process where air is forced to rise or sink (especially important with thermals and cumulus clouds) adiabatic laws of cooling and heating are obeyed.

The answer to why rising (or sinking) air obeys the adiabatic laws lies in the great size of air parcels. In met. terms thermals may be relatively small parcels, and their temperature is only a few degrees different from their environment. The only way they could exchange heat with their surroundings would be by conduction or radiation, both of which are vanishingly small and only occur on the edges anyway. Thus effectively a rising thermal (or Cu cloud) is isolated from its surroundings and cools only because the heat energy it contains becomes spread more thinly through its envelope as it rises into lower pressure. The converse occurs when sinking air is squeezed by increasing pressure. Then adiabatic warming occurs, showing up most markedly when strong subsidence inversions set in during anticyclonic weather.

ADIABATIC LAPSE RATES See *Lapse rates*.

ADVECTION Movement of a weather process sideways as opposed to convection which involves vertical movement. It is used most often when describing fog that is transported to your site, rather than radiation fog which develops over the site itself. Advection fog affects coastal heights when warm, wet winds blow in from seaward. It also comes with frontal systems and when pure mT (maritime Tropical) airmasses blow over hill and mountain slopes.

AEROFOIL (Airfoil in US) Any cambered surface designed to generate lift.

AIR MAP SYMBOLS Indicate where gliding activity is taking place and appear on aeronautical charts produced by the Civil Aviation Authority. The following are the symbols used:

Fig. A.1

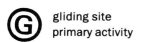 gliding site primary activity

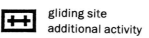 gliding site additional activity

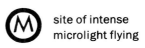 site of intense microlight flying

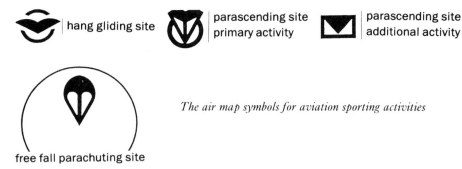

hang gliding site

parascending site
primary activity

parascending site
additional activity

free fall parachuting site

The air map symbols for aviation sporting activities

AIRMASSES Originate in source regions which have extreme characteristics. They may be full of moisture (maritime) or relatively dry (continental). They may be from southern source regions (tropical) or from northern climes (polar or arctic) (see fig. A.2).

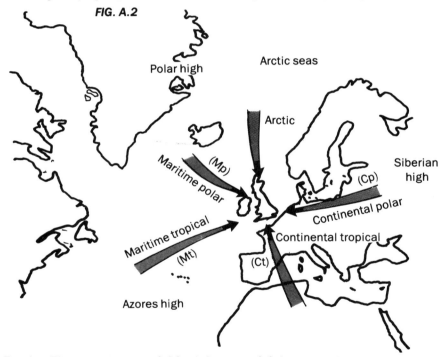

FIG. A.2

Polar high

Arctic seas

Arctic

Maritime polar (Mp)

Siberian high

(Cp)

Continental polar

Maritime tropical (Mt)

Continental tropical

(Ct)

Azores high

Fig. A.2 The major airmasses of Atlantic Europe and their source regions

A pure airmass possesses its characteristics through its entire depth; a 'warm' airmass at altitude will merely be warmer than an adjacent 'cold' airmass. Both may be below -40°C. The principle airmasses of the Atlantic European area are as follows.

The *maritime Polar (mP)* airmass is unstable and creates large cumulus (Cu) and cumulonimbus (Cb) clouds (see photograph). It normally comes on NW winds behind retreating low pressure centres and is introduced behind a cold front. Inland, it is best to fly such an airmass either early or late, when the warmth of the sun does not induce the strength of updraughts and downdraughts that occur in the middle of the day. The mP airmass often stays for several days, but stabilises with time.

The *returning maritime Polar (rmP)* airmass starts from the same polar stable as the mP, but it is forced to come on a very long seatrack southwards and eastwards around the more or less permanent low pressure area south of Iceland. During this long journey it loses its extreme instability and its trademark is fair-weather Cu cloud which is of limited vertical extent (see photograph 7). This is one of the best airmasses in which to fly, as winds are usually light to moderate and the convection aids soaring or at least slows the rate of sink.

The *maritime Tropical (Mt)* airmass is stable and its trademarks are layer clouds at all levels. Cloud types include stratus (St) (see photograph 8), nimbostratus (Ns) (see photograph 4), altostratus (As) (see photograph 3), cirrus (Ci) (see photograph 1) and cirrostratus (Cs) (see photograph 2). In its purest form it comes on SW winds from sub-tropical ocean wastes and can easily produce hazardous flying conditions because of fog and low St cloud to which it is very prone. It is the airmass that creates the clouds of fronts.

The *continental Polar* (cP) airmass is usually dry, cold or cool, and comes mainly on easterly winds from the depths of the Continent. It can, however, produce heat waves in summer and intense cold in winter. It has many characteristics sometimes resembling rmP air after a 500-mile or more sea track.

The *continental Tropical* (cT) airmass is dry and is often the airmass that goes with extreme heat in summer or with unseasonal warmth at any time of year. Despite the heat, it is often quite stable. However, there may be low-level 'explosive' instability which makes for dangerous flying.

Of these, the mP and mT airmasses are the most often experienced, as they lie on opposite sides of the Polar front along which the depressions breed. The warm sectors of depressions are home to mT air and the rest of the depression's circulation is different forms of mP air.

The above descriptions of mT and mP airmasses are of the pure forms, but on many occasions the air you have is only an echo of a once proud airmass. Many airmasses have suffered from subsiding air sinking onto them from great heights, thus producing subsidence inversions which limit the instability to relatively low levels. Such modified airmasses are often characterised by layers of stratocumulus (Sc) cloud.

TABLE A.1 A RUN-DOWN ON AIRMASSES

Abbreviation	Name	Typical weather	Source
mT	maritime Tropical	Extensively cloudy with rain and drizzle. Poor visibility and fog.	Azores High
mP	maritime Polar	Showers and bright periods. Good visibility.	Polar High
rmP	returning maritime Polar	Cool but fair. Good Visibility.	As mP but modified by Atlantic Ocean
cP	continental Polar	Sometimes fair in summer. Intensely cold in winter.	Northern Europe or Siberian High
cT	continental Tropical	Very warm for time of year. Often cloudless.	Southern Europe or N. Africa

AIRSPEED The speed with which a glider penetrates the air. A glider will always have an airspeed, but it need not have a groundspeed. See *Groundspeed*.

AIRSPEED INDICATORS Important devices which show the speed of the air as it affects the wing, sail or parafoil. However, while these are practical devices for gliders and hang gliders, they are not for paragliders. Paraglider pilots have to learn to judge airspeed by sound and feel. An airspeed indicator on the ground becomes an anemometer (see photograph A.1).

ALPINE WEATHER Very changeable and must never be relied on for long. Here is a Safety Notice from the British Association of Paragliding Clubs, dated 20 June 1990:

DANGEROUS SUMMER ALPINE FLYING CONDITIONS

As a result of a recent fatal flying accident involving a BAPC member, all pilots are warned that flying in the Alps is potentially dangerous.

It is essential that any pilot contemplating Alpine flying must:

1. Obtain advice on local conditions from local paragliding/hang gliding centres/clubs.

2. Be aware of the turbulence/thermic conditions prevalent in the area – especially in the late morning and afternoon.

3. Be practised in dealing with partial or full tucks and canopy reflation drills.

4. Know that for an F.1 pilot to fly unsupervised is highly dangerous and absolutely forbidden under any circumstances.

The Alpine chain, together with the Pyrenees and the Massif Central on the west and the Dolomites and Dinaric Alps on the east, effectively separates Europe from the Mediterranean. South of the Alps, the weather is more settled than on the northern side, but even if flying the Mediterranean side it is still important to consult forecasts as often as possible. The year in the Alps goes something like this. **January** – often high pressure and dry, cold weather. The valleys often lie under cloud, but the heights see sunshine and high temperatures for the time of year. **February** – frequent snowfalls occur. The snow that falls lasts well into the summer. **March** – a wet month, with snowfall mainly confined to the heights. The first Föhn storms produce wet snow avalanches. **April** – another wet month with frequent Föhn storms. **May** – there is often a cold spell around the middle of the month, with snow down into the valleys. **June** – much the same as May, but more chance of showers and some severe thunderstorms. **July** – is often wet and humid. **August** – the first three weeks are usually good, but the end of the month often sees storms and even snow at altitude. **September** – usually a fine month, with good visibility, but the first chill of winter is felt at night. **October** – the autumn regime of good weather continues, but this is the last month for going at all high. The nights are often very cold. **November** – the first month of winter, with poor visibility, the first real snowfalls and Föhn storms. **December** – much the same as November until Christmas. Anticyclonic weather after Christmas brings increasing cold.

ALTIMETERS Devices which record the height to which you have ascended. They respond to a drop in pressure with height and may be based on an aneroid capsule or on a transducer that makes the device entirely electronic. Simple models indicate every 100ft (30m) and some are accurate enough to go down to 1ft (0.3m) limits. What you choose depends on the glider you fly and on your state of training. Paraglider pilots only need a rugged device of medium sensitivity.

ANABATIC WINDS Winds which blow uphill in mountainous or hilly areas, from low areas in shadow to heights in sunshine. They normally only amount to light breezes and are confined to quiet weather.

ANA FRONTS Fronts in which the air is mainly ascending. They therefore are fronts which produce the worst kinds of associated weather. Ana cold fronts are especially dangerous, as they may give little warning of their approach and updraughts along their leading edges are often of the order of 20 knots. They are also accompanied by surface squalls, heavy hail and rain, as well as in some cases thunder. See *Kata fronts*, *Warm fronts*, *Cold fronts*, *Occluded fronts* and figs 3.2 and 3.3.

ANEMOMETERS Devices for recording wind speed. The indications given under Beaufort scale are very rough and the criteria, such as smoke or trees in motion, may not be visible. Simple anemometers are an important part of the glider pilot's kit and take up very little room. When using an anemometer, make sure that you get a reading which is representative for your take-off and landing sites. See page 55 for advice on assessing wind speeds.

ANGLE OF ATTACK Angle the relative wind makes with the chord of an aerofoil. See figs 5.1 and 5.13.

ANEMOGRAPHS Devices for drawing continuous graphs of the variation in wind speed and direction. The resulting graphs constitute an anemogram; fig. A.3 depicts a typical light weather anemogram when a seabreeze set in a few miles inland from a south-facing coast.

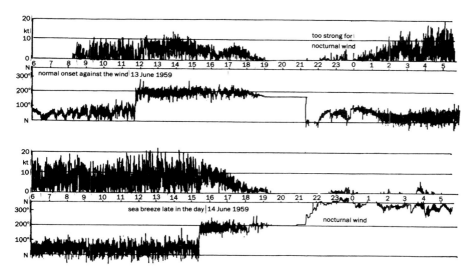

Fig. A.3 Anemograms are drawn by wind vanes and wind speed transducers connected to pens running over special charts. They give a picture of what the wind did in speed and direction changes for, in these cases, twenty-four hours. The top anemogram shows a seabreeze setting in at Thorney Island against a NE wind of an average speed of 5 knots. This wind had one of the abnormal patterns of variation mentioned on page 71. The evening calm is typical, but the wind that got up in the early hours of the next day was due to a strengthening gradient being too strong to be a nocturnal wind.

In the lower case the wind opposing the breeze was somewhat stronger and so it was after 1500Z that the breeze managed to overcome it. When the breeze sets in that late it cannot be expected to last for very long. It also relapsed into an evening calm to be followed, in this case, by a true nocturnal wind off the South Downs

ANTICYCLONES High pressure areas in which the air from extreme altitude sinks. In this process it warms up by adiabatic compression and this raises the air to a temperature above its dewpoint. The result is that high- and medium-level clouds are eroded and eventually they disappear. However, this does not mean that low clouds will also disappear. Many anticyclones have within their circulation large areas of stratocumulus cloud which are very persistent. In late spring and summer the power of the sun can often 'burn off' these low cloud layers, leading to blue skies in which Cu clouds may not develop. There will be 'dry' anticyclones at other times of year which will also be largely cloudless, but whether it is cloudy or fair depends very much on where the air in the anticyclone originated.

Anticyclones or 'highs' either travel or they remain in one locality for days, weeks and occasionally months. The latter are called 'blocking' highs, as they block the advance of the upper westerlies, the jet streams are diverted north and south of them, and the accompanying depressions go, too. This leads to unseasonal weather in other localities. For example, when a block occurs over Britain and surrounding areas, weather is often poor in Spain, even if it is summer.

The sinking air in a slow-moving or quasi-stationary high may become so warmed by descent that it forms an impenetrable inversion (a subsidence inversion) through which thermals cannot penetrate despite the air temperature rising into the eighties and nineties (°F). Flying in these conditions can be hazardous, because of the 'explosive' nature of the low-level thermals that do develop. In most highs there will be some form of inversion not many thousands of feet from the ground and it is this inversion in which the persistent cloud-sheets form and stay.

Highs are also regions of outflowing winds. Often the wind is not strong, and near the centre it will be calm or very light so that local winds have every chance to develop and take over the existing wind scene.

ANTICYCLONIC Term used to describe either the type of weather associated with high pressure regions or the sense in which the isobars curve on a weather map (see fig. A.4). In the case of anticyclonic (as opposed to cyclonic) curvature, the isobars curve in an attempt

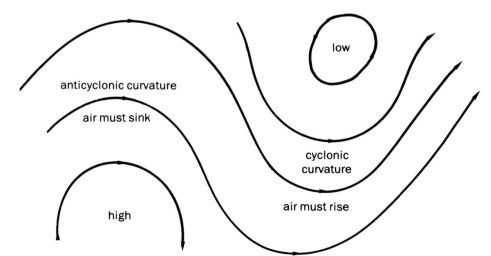

Fig. A.4 To illustrate what is meant by cyclonic and anticyclonic curvature of isobars

to enclose higher pressure. Under anticyclonic curvature, whatever weather there is tends to improve, as air must sink from above. This does not, however, mean that there will be less cloud cover. In fact, there may be more low cloud under anticyclonic curvature than elsewhere, because of such effects as Cu spreading into Sc under a subsidence inversion.

ASPECT RATIO Span of an aerofoil divided by its chord or, for wings which taper, the span squared divided by the surface area. A wide, narrow wing has a high aspect ratio. Beginners' parafoils should have an aspect ratio of between 2 and 3, although better design is increasing aspect ratio for all stages of expertise. High aspect ratio aerofoils are more efficient than low ones, but low aspect ratio wings are more forgiving.

ATLANTIC EUROPE Term for those countries of western Europe that have coasts facing the Atlantic or which are within the throw of the Atlantic weather systems. These include Britain and the coastal areas of Europe, from Norway down to Spain and Portugal.

BACKING WIND Wind that shifts direction anti-clockwise. Backing winds are particularly associated with the onset of deteriorating weather.

BAROGRAPHS Record atmospheric pressure on a chart called a barogram and enable you to see what has happened to the pressure in the past. They do not, however, give much help with the trend of future events; they are devices for established met. facilities. The symbols for pressure tendency plotted on station circles are representations of what you might see on the barogram at the time (see fig. B.1 on page 130).

BAROMETERS Measure atmospheric pressure and their active elements may be an evacuated metal box or capsule, or a pressure-sensitive transducer. The capsule is the heart of the aneroid (non-liquid) barometer. When the pressure increases, the capsule collapses slightly, and when it falls, the capsule expands. These minute movements are transmitted and amplified through a linkage, and are exhibited on a dial which may be calibrated in millibars (mb), or inches or millimetres of mercury (in. or mm Hg). Millibars are preferred, as they accord with the practice of the met. services. The millimetre of mercury unit follows from the fact that for scientific purposes standard atmospheric pressure is 760mm Hg.

$$760\text{mm Hg} = 29.92\text{ in. Hg} = 1013.6\text{ mb}$$

The legends of 'fair', 'rain', 'change', etc. on the dials of many domestic barometers should be treated with extreme caution. The only attribute of the barometer which has a real weather forecasting value is the change in its value since the last reading. This is called the 'barometric tendency' or just the 'tendency'. See *Altimeter, Barometric tendency, Pressure.*

BAROMETRIC TENDENCY For met. purposes this is the change in the height of the barometer over the last three hours and on weather charts that is what is displayed (see fig. B.1 on page 130). However, if you are watching a barometer to see whether it is falling (often a sign of coming deterioration in the present conditions) or rising (a sign of improvement), three hours is a long time to wait, and a rule of thumb is that should the barometer fall by about 1mb/hour, then expect the imminent arrival of winds that are too strong to fly. It must be stressed that the barometer wanders up and down during relatively fair weather without the changes meaning very much. What you have to look for is a fall that continues hour by hour and becomes steeper with time. This indicates the onset of a bad weather system and therefore suggests that paraglider pilots might be advised to be packing up and hiking off back to base before it really gets nasty.

BEAUFORT SCALE OF WIND FORCE Accepted scale for assessing the strength of the surface wind. It was originally devised by Admiral Beaufort for men-of-war but has been adapted since. The version on page 131 is suitable for the needs of glider pilots.

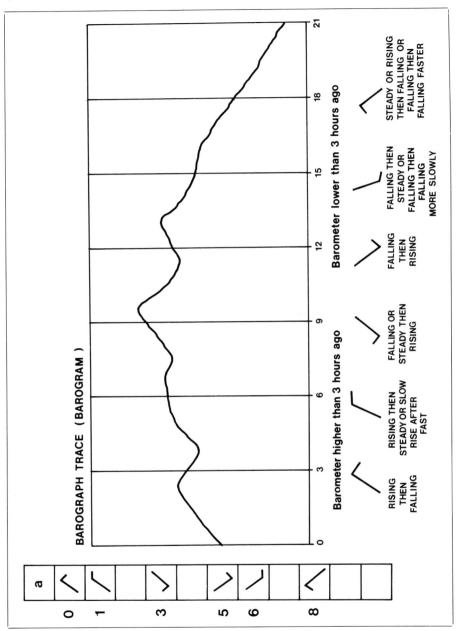

Fig. B.1 *A fictitious barogram showing which features of the barograph trace give rise to the symbols used to represent tendency. The boxes headed (a) are the reporting code figures*

BERNOUILLE'S THEOREM Concerns the changes in energy along a streamline. In fact, a streamline can be defined as a tube of air along which Bernouille's equation applies.

A volume of air which is moving and which is not having air fed into it or extracted from

Beaufort scale of wind force

Symbol	Beaufort number	General description	Limit of mean speed (knots)	Land signs	Symbols used on charts	
⊚	0	Calm	Less than 1	Smoke rises vertically. Leaves do not stir	⊚	Calm
	1	Light air	1-3	Smoke drifts. Wind vanes do not respond		1-2 kt.
	2	Light breeze	4-6	Wind felt on the face. Leaves rustle. Light flags not extended. Wind vanes respond		3-7
	3	Gentle breeze	7-10	Light flags extended. Leaves in constant motion		8-12
	4	Moderate breeze	11-16	Most flags extend fully. Small branches move. Dust and loose paper may be raised		13-17
	5	Fresh breeze	17-21	Small trees in leaf sway. Tops of tall trees in noticeable motion		18-22
	6	Strong breeze	22-27	Large branches in motion. Whistling heard in wires		23-27
	7	Near gale (American usage: Moderate gale)	28-33	Whole trees in motion. Inconvenience felt when walking against wind		28-32
	8	Gale (Fresh gale)	34-40	Twigs broken off trees. Generally impeded progress on foot. Rarely experienced inland		33-37
	9	Strong gale (Strong gale)	41-47	Chimney pots and slates removed. Fences blown down, etc.		38-42
						43-47

it has constant energy, i.e. the energy it possesses after a change is the same as it was before the change – it is simply re-distributed among the three ways in which its energy can change. Bernouille's equation states this formally as:

pressure energy + kinetic energy + potential energy = constant.

When air does not ascend or descend appreciably, then its potential energy (PE) does not change. So, for streamline flow over aerofoils, any increase in the air speed, i.e. kinetic energy (KE), must lead to a drop in pressure (because pressure is proportional to pressure energy) (see fig. 5.12). Thus an aerofoil is a surface which, due to its camber, can make the air travel faster over its upper surface. However, the flow must remain laminar, i.e. must travel as streamlines and must not be allowed to become turbulent (see fig. 5.13).

When air streams over mountain and hill ridges, and remains in laminar flow, there is considerable change in its potential energy, and so all three components of Bernouille's equation come into play. As the air ascends the windward side of the ridge and its PE increases (see fig. 8.6), the streamlines tend to crowd over the summits and this means an increase in wind speed. So, both PE and KE increase, which means that pressure must fall as the air ascends and breaks over the summits. On the lee sides, the PE is lost as the air descends, but of course the land may not be the same height on the two sides, which could mean that the descending air did not lose all the PE it lost climbing the windward sides. Or, it might lose more, depending on the land levels on the two sides.

BLOCKING HIGHS Immense anticyclones that remain quasi-stationary over parts of the temperate latitudes, often for long periods. They bring many weeks of settled weather to the areas they cover. See *Anticyclones*.

BLUE THERMALS Occur on fine days when conditions are not right for the development of Cu cloud. There are no visible signs of these thermals until you fly into them. They may be 'explosive' when it is hot.

BOUNDARY LAYER A term used in a met. sense to describe the surface air-deck where airflow changes rapidly, due to the friction of the Earth and the objects that are on it. Strictly speaking, the air in direct contact with the ground is stationary, but it has rapidly to acquire the speed of the wind. How it does this up to a height of 30ft (10m) over long and short grass is shown in fig. 6.8. Over long grass (2ft high) the wind at 30ft has doubled its speed over that at 3ft and over short grass it is approaching one and a half times its speed at 3ft. After that, the increase slows down. However, because of large objects such as trees and buildings, plus the effects of limited convection currents, the air-deck through which the Earth still affects the wind is hundreds and sometimes thousands of feet deep. Throughout the depth of this air-deck the air is mixed up by great eddies and thermal currents, and so it is often called the 'mixing layer'. See also page 9 and *Variable wind.*

BURSTS Term used in several different contexts. A *cloud burst* occurs when the updraughts in thunder clouds are reduced or cut off, and the cloud deposits much of its stored moisture as a prodigious amount of rain over a limited area. As much as an inch or more may fall in an many hours.

Bursts of rain is a phrase much used on domestic forecasts to indicate when some form of intermittent rainfall is expected. It may mean showers, thundery showers, intermittent rain, etc. – anything where the rain is not continuous.

Microbursts are a small version of so-called 'downbursts' that occur with supercells (see *Thunderstorms*) in the tropics. Although not as bad as downbursts, microbursts can produce descending and rotating winds whose central downdraughts exceed 50kt and which therefore produce spreading winds of much the same speed. There may be rain, but some microbursts occur from Cb above a high cloudbase in dry conditions. Luckily, they are rare.

BUYS BALLOT'S LAW The well-known truism that if you stand with the surface wind blowing into your back then

pressure is low on your left.

This applies to the northern hemisphere and also, if you stand facing the wind, to the southern hemisphere. It was first formulated by a Dutch professor, Buys Ballot, of Utrecht University in 1857. It does not apply to seabreezes, land breezes, mountain and valley winds, etc. which are due to local influences. It is seen in action whenever the wind is depicted blowing along the direction of the isobars on a TV or other weather chart. See *Isobars, Anticyclones, Depressions, Weather maps.*

CAMBER The degree of curvature on an aerofoil. Low speed wings need high camber, i.e. they are thick, while high speed sections will be of low camber and as thin as aeronautical engineering will allow.

CANOPY Another term for the 'wing' of a paraglider. It is a throwback to parachutes.

CASTELLANUS Form of altocumulus where lines of cloud in the medium levels grow small turret-tops, looking like castle battlements. They show instability at medium levels and the risk of thunderstorms later. They are often seen with floccus. In photograph C.1, despite the brightness, there were heavy showers occurring locally from unstable medium cloud. You should think carefully about flying if this form of sky lies either over or near your site. Castles can be nasties!

CELLS Individual inflated units of a canopy.

CELSIUS (CENTIGRADE) SCALE The scale of temperature that marks zero degrees

C.1 Lines of altocumulus floccus and castellanus stream across from left to right. The floccus is in the lowest and highest parts of the picture, while the castellanus lies behind

at the freezing point of water and 100 degrees at the boiling point. It is the standard scale in Europe and most other countries, and is used by the scientific community. The conversions between Celsius and Fahrenheit are shown below.

-40	-35	-30	-25	-20	-15	-10	-5	$0°$ C		0	5	10	15	20	25	30	35	$40°$ C
-40	-31	-22	-13	-4	$+5$	$+14$	$+23$	$32°$ F		32	41	50	59	68	77	86	95	$104°$ F

A useful guide to 'sensation value' in still air is as follows.

degrees C	*sensation value*
0 and below	freezing
5	cold
10	chilly
15	mild
20	warm
25	hot
30	very hot

CENTRE OF GRAVITY (C of G) More correctly called the Centre of Mass. It is the point through which the force of gravity can be assumed to act, even though the mass of the glider, its pilot and equipment is obviously distributed over a wide area.

CHORD Direct distance from the leading edge to the trailing edge of an aerofoil.

CLOUDS Formed by any process which makes air rise. The main methods of formation are:

(a) warm air being lifted over cold air, as happens at warm and cold fronts. Such frontal lifting leads to extensive layer clouds, as well as cirrus and other ice-crystal clouds. It is the way in which deep masses of nimbostratus (Ns) are formed, sometimes with cumulonimbus (Cb) embedded within them.

C.2 Scattered cumulus cloud indicates a relatively dry airstream but one that is still unstable enough to provide thermic conditions

(b) cool air flowing over a warmer surface, which leads to heap clouds and possibly showers or thunderstorms. Most of the good flying days occur under this regime. This leads to convective lifting (see photograph C.2).

C.3 This is turbulence cloud formed by eddies in the wind and having very little form. It may or may not cover the tops

C.4 Cloud evaporates in the air descending a hill ridge in Wales

(c) turbulent eddies produced by the wind blowing over the terrain which lift surface air enough to produce low billow clouds that often cover the whole sky. This is turbulence cloud and it may cover the hill tops (see photograph C.3).

(d) orographic lifting which leads to extensive low cloud, and rain and fog on windward slopes and over the tops of hills and mountains. It is over the ridges of massifs that clouds deposit their rain (or snow) and often it is much dryer, even with sunny intervals, on the leeward sides. It may be possible to find some slopes facing the wind downwind of a major hill or mountain range where conditions can be quite promising, despite the fact that some miles/kilometres to windward the slopes are deluged with rain and out in fog (see photograph C.4).

(e) interference between two layers of air moving at different speeds. Wave motion occurs in the interface between them and forms of stratocumulus (Sc) and altocumulus (Ac) appear which look like waves resembling sand on the seashore when the tide has receded (see photograph C.5 on p.136).

(f) wave streaming in the lee of hill and mountain ridges. This leads to lens-shaped clouds (Sc lenticularis, Ac lenticularis, as well as Cc lenticularis) forming in the tops of the long wavelength waves that may occur many, many miles/kilometres downwind of the ridge producing them (see photograph 9).

(g) convergence of two opposing airstreams such as occurs along seabreeze fronts. In effect, surface winds collide and the only means of escape is upwards. This leads to a line of heavy-looking heap clouds from which a slight shower may occur. In certain circumstances the seabreeze frontal clouds may be the only clouds in the sky (see photograph 20).

There are other ways in which specific cloud types are formed and often it is in hilly terrain that such clouds appear, but the methods outlined above are by far the most important.

Clouds are divided into three height decks and it is not possible to be too precise about what the divisions of height are (refer to fig. 2.1):

C.5 When winds blow at different speeds above and below a cloud layer, waves are often set up, as shown here

(1) low clouds which include cumulus (Cu), stratus (St) and stratocumulus (Sc). Clouds in this bracket generally exist below 7000ft (2km) and their names have no prefixes.

(2) medium-level clouds which are all prefixed by the height designation 'alto'. The layer forms are altostratus (As) and the heap forms are altocumulus (Ac). They generally exist below 20,000ft (6km).

(3) high-level clouds which are, in general, called cirroform and are composed of ice crystals as opposed to the water-droplet clouds of the medium- and low-levels. They include cirrus (Ci), cirrostratus (Cs) and cirrocumulus (Cc). They generally exist below 40000ft (12km).

(4) deep rain-bearing clouds which span the above brackets. The layer form is nimbostratus (Ns), while the heap form is cumulonimbus (Cb). Both forms may be solid between the surface and the tropopause.

CLOUD COVER Measured in octas or eighths of the sky covered. The merest trace of a cloud in an otherwise blue sky counts as 1 octa, while the slightest chink in an otherwise totally overcast sky will be given as 7 octas. Otherwise, the observer estimates how much of the sky is covered and reports accordingly. The symbols used in the centres of station circles on weather maps are shown at the top of the next page.

CLOUDINESS Tends to go with a continuation of the existing weather.

Winds do not usually change much under 7/8 to 8/8ths cloud cover. When a change in the pattern of cloudiness comes along, there is often a change of wind as well. Cloudiness damps out the diurnal variation in the weather elements, so that the wind speed remains much the same all day and the temperature does not increase much either. It prevents radiation, which otherwise may result in fog or frost. However, when existing early-morning fog does not clear during the morning, the reason is usually that the sun cannot penetrate a cloud layer above it.

code figure	N			
0	○	5	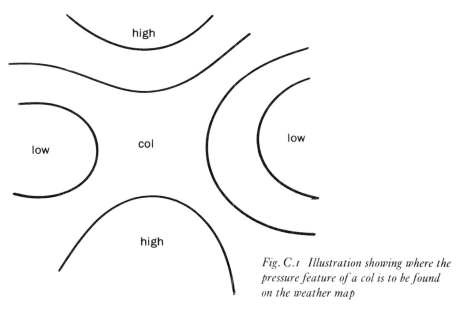	
1	◐(vertical)	6		
2		7		
3		8	●	
4		9	⊗	
		/	⊗	

9 = sky obscured
/ = sky not observed

Symbols used in station circles on weather maps

Cloudiness is also affected by mountain and hill ranges, with the maximum cloud on the windward slopes and over the tops, and much less cloud in the lee (see photograph C.4). It may also change when an oceanic airstream comes ashore. Airstreams that are cloudless over the sea may develop cloud because of the warmth of the land.

COL Name borrowed from geographers. It is the 'saddle-backed' pressure region between two lows and two highs, corresponding to the same feature on a land contour map (see fig. C.1).

high

low   col   low

high

Fig. C.1 Illustration showing where the pressure feature of a col is to be found on the weather map

COLD FRONTS Divide warm air from cold or cool air when the front is moving away from the cold air. This follows because a front gets its name from the temperature of the air behind it. Cold fronts are usually more active than warm fronts or occlusions (see *Ana fronts*) and there is often quite a large change in wind direction when they pass. With ana fronts this change comes sharply under the cloud-wall that marks the leading edge (see photograph 12). At the leading edge, and ahead of it, there is often a squall of wind which will perhaps double or even treble the previous speed. The squall stems from the downdraughts that fall along the leading edge and compensate for the strong updraughts within the cloud-mass (see fig. 3.3). After this wild phase has passed, lighter rain occurs, and eventually it dies out to nothing. Once the back edge of the cloud-sheet clears, the sun will come out, but it will take time for the ground to warm sufficiently for convection to occur. Thus there is often a clear slot behind the clouds of a cold front before heap clouds begin to build. With a great deal of moisture on the ground from the cold front's rain, and with unstable air, the heap clouds can grow into sizeable showers which can be dangerous for flying.

Cold fronts tend to be ana on the coasts that face the Atlantic and to become less active as they traverse land areas. They will be less active in the lee of high massifs and at the same time subsiding air over them will gradually reduce them to kata fronts.

For information about the problems that may be induced by wind shifts at cold fronts see table 4.2 on page 30.

COMMA CLOUDS Appear on satellite cloud pictures. They look like large commas: the 'dot' of the comma is the cloud shield over a depression while the 'tail' is a trailing cold front. A now notorious one is shown in photograph C.6. It accompanied the depression that led to the Fastnet yacht race disaster. The picture was taken by TIROS-N at visible wave lengths on the afternoon of 13 August 1979.

CONDENSATION Occurs whenever a parcel of moist air becomes super-saturated with water vapour. By far the most common reason is that the air has fallen in temperature; the process is epitomised by dew when the ground temperature has fallen below the dewpoint overnight. Condensation can occur quite early in the evening and canopies or wings laid out for evening flying may gather a surface film of water, so lowering their aerofoil properties.

Condensation of water vapour into cloud droplets (or dew) requires the intervention of so-called condensation nuclei to allow the process of droplet formation to begin (see *Rain*).

Condensation can be observed occurring in an airstream at the leading edges of lenticular clouds (see fig. C.2). These clouds will only be in existence where the air is rising, cooling and condensing. So, there is no cloud in the rising air-wave until it has cooled below its dewpoint. In passing through the volume of the cloud, the air is below its dewpoint, but as it sinks on the back of the wave, it warms to a temperature above its dewpoint and the cloud droplets evaporate. 'Lenties' are simply markers for the crests of the waves in wave-streaming conditions, which is why they only move when the waves move. The opposite of condensation is *Evaporation*.

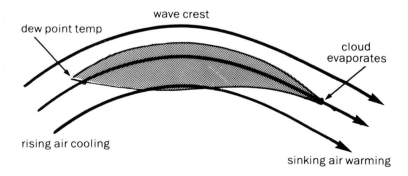

Fig. C.2 How a lenticular cloud is formed and the reasons for its shape

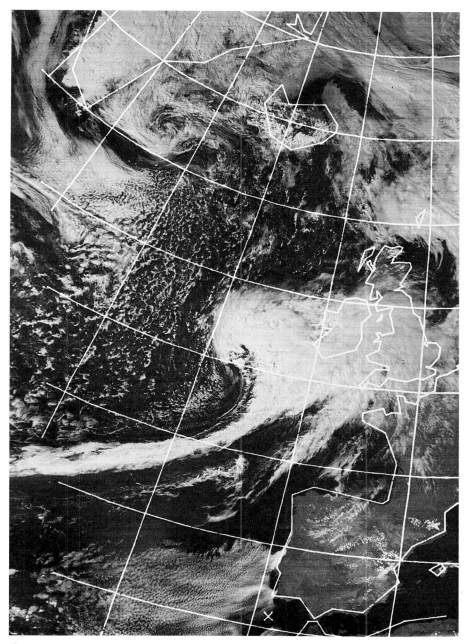

C.6 *Visible image of the storm that caused the Fastnet disaster of 13–14 August 1979 taken at 1537Z on the 13th. Note the long 'trails' of cirrus behind the cold front where it emerges from the 'comma-shaped' cloud shield. On the extreme left the increase in the width of the cold front is an indication that the front is waving. Large numbers of big Cb clouds stream down in streets behind the low which is tracking roughly north-eastwards*

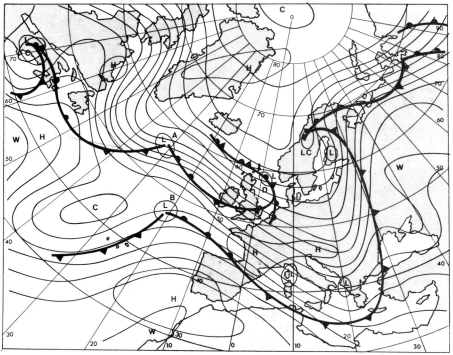

Fig. C.3 The contours of the 300 mb surface on a day in October, showing features of the upper winds and how they relate to the surface pressure systems. Low A is a developing depression under a 'race-track' of contours where the temperate latitude jet stream is situated. Low B is in much the same position under the sub-tropical jet. However, Low D is a depression formed on the point of occlusion – which sometimes happens – and is north of the jet, as is Low C which will be filling. W and C in the contour features stand for Warm domes and Cold pools respectively. Where W and H coincide, as on the extreme left, there will be no motion and this will be a blocking high, but the highs over France and Central Europe are travelling under the impetus of the upper winds. The low over Maine is also coincident with a cold pool and will be equally stuck and unable to move.

CONTOURS Equivalent to isobars on upper air weather maps (see fig. C.3). On such maps all points are the same atmospheric pressure. So, just as on a topographic map, meteorological contours are lines joining places of equal height. However, in this case the height is that of a pressure level, and pressure levels go up over warm air columns and sink over cold air columns. Thus a contour map of a pressure surface must be envisaged as gently rolling ground doming up over the warmer air columns and dishing down into areas where the air below the level is colder. Such contour maps are drawn for standard pressure levels of 850, 700, 500, 300, 200 and 100 millibars, and on them the winds blow along the contours to keep *low temperature* air on their *left*. Just like isobars, contours indicate stronger upper winds when they pack more closely together. The 850mb charts indicate the winds at about 5000ft, which could be useful when compared with the isobars on a surface map to indicate changes in wind direction between 2000 and 5000ft. The 700mb contours give the winds at the 10000ft level of alto clouds while the 500mb winds are the ones which tend to steer depressions and lie around 20000ft. The 300mb contours show the winds at jet stream and cirrus levels, i.e. around 30000ft, while the 200 and 100mb levels go up to around 50000ft.

Contour maps, both actual and forecast, constantly pour off the printers of weatherfax machines giving ideas of what the upper winds will be doing for many days ahead.

CONVERGENCE Met. term which indicates that more air is entering any vertical column of air than is leaving it. This leads to rising surface pressure, so a developing high or ridge is a region of convergence. At low altitude, convergence occurs when winds blow towards one another, e.g. when seabreezes meet opposing winds. In this case, the result is ascent along the line of convergence, leading to heavier cloud masses there and even to showers or thunderstorms (see also *Divergence*).

CONVEYER BELTS It has long been a mystery as to how depressions are fed with air from their surrounding anticyclones. Studies of air motions in lows have shown that air enters them via two great rivers of air called conveyer belts. In fig. C.4 a cold conveyer rises slowly up ahead of the warm front and turns at altitude to follow the high-level upper winds. This draws its air from the high ahead of the low. The warm conveyer belt draws its air from the high to the south, and flows up ahead of the cold front. It runs over the cold belt to again turn and add to the high-level winds. At the same time, a lesser stream of cold, dry air is drawn in behind the cold front. Thus figs. such as 2.3 are purely diagrammatic and do not indicate in any real way the actual air motions that are going on. However, note

Fig. C.4 The conveyor-belt model of the airflow at altitude over a typical depression

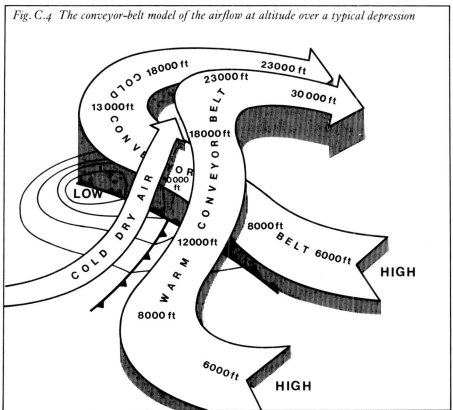

the heights at which the conveyers start. They are well above the flying deck for hang gliders and paragliders.

CROSS COUNTRY (XC) Flying beyond the limits of the launch site, using thermal or other lift and usually not returning to the site.

CROSSED WINDS' RULES Because of the dynamic and thermal structure of depressions, it is found that when major changes are on the way the winds at cirrus levels (around 30,000ft) must blow at an angle across the gradient wind direction. The most potent orientation is when the upper wind (U) is crossed to the lower (L) at right angles (see fig. C.5).

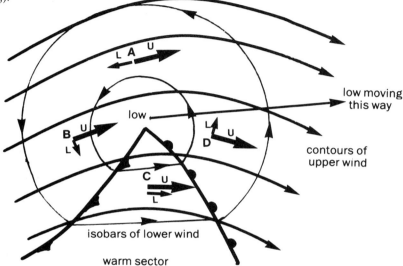

Fig. C.5 Upper (U) and lower (L) wind flow of an idealised depression. At D the crossing of the two winds indicates coming deterioration, while at B we have the crossing for improvement

Ahead of an approaching warmer airmass (which usually means a deteriorating weather situation), the following rule applies.

Crossed winds' rule for deterioration: stand back to the lower wind and if the upper wind comes from the *left* hand the weather usually deteriorates.

Conversely, ahead of an approaching colder airmass (which usually means the development of anticyclonic conditions and therefore improvement) another rule applies:

Crossed winds' rule for improvement: stand back to the lower wind and if the upper wind comes from the *right* then the weather usually improves.

In fig. C.5 the bold lines are contours of the 300mb surface or, put more simply, the way the upper winds blow at cirrus (and jetstream) levels. They obey the rule that:

upper winds blow to keep *low* temperature on their *left*

and so the upper winds over a warm sector must bend to enclose the warm air. Thus the most likely direction for cirrus to approach from is NW, while in the developing gradient ahead of the coming low the gradient wind is often SW. It will be seen that this obeys the crossed winds' rule for deterioration.

The greater the contrast the temperatures between the cold and warm parts of a depression, the greater will be the vigour of the latter. The jetstream will be stronger for one thing, and the cirrus carried along in the 100 + knot upper winds will be easily detected as being in motion. Such easily detectable motion indicates strong development of the situation and thus strong to gale winds at the surface later.

The improvement rule is very useful when a depression is moving away. The cirrus along the back edge of the cloud shield of the cold front can often (as seen in photographs C.6 and 22) be monitored and combined with a known gradient wind direction to estimate the degree of improvement there may be. If, say, the cirrus is coming from SW (as it often does), while the gradient wind is NW the crossed winds' rule for improvement is obeyed and usually a good ridge or even a full-blown high develops, giving several good flying days. However, if the upper and lower winds do not differ greatly in direction and even become more nearly aligned with time, then expect another depression to be following this one.

While the winds of full-blown depressions have been cited above, the rules work with lesser systems and with gradient winds from all directions. In thundery conditions, with much castellanus or floccus streaming in on medium-level winds, the rules work well with the upper wind now being the direction of movement of the alto clouds. This allows you to make up your mind if the cloud really means a coming thundery trough or not.

Two other orientations of U and L can be seen in fig. C.5 to the north and south of the low centre. In the former case, the two winds are opposed, inferring a low centre to the south. In the latter, the two winds are in the same direction, indicating a low centre to the north. Where U and L are roughly in the same direction, it indicates no change at the present time, but that does not preclude change in the coming hours: the situation has to be continuously monitored.

As cirrus cloud is clear of being steered by the terrain, so the crossed winds' rules are of great service in mountainous regions where lower winds can be steered by high peaks and ridges. The problems will always be to obtain the true direction of the lower wind. It will be found reliably from the isobars on a weather map and, if nothing else, note the direction given on, say, last night's TV forecast chart in case it is needed next day when you may be out of touch with a means of finding the gradient wind direction. Remember in this context that the gradient wind is veered to the surface wind and allowance must be made. A perfect means of finding the gradient wind (except near mountains) is to monitor closely the flight of Cu or other low clouds.

CROSSWIND A wind angled across the normal launch or flight path. For take-off or landing a paraglider, this usually means a wind at an angle greater than 30° to the direct line onto the launch site.

CUMULONIMBUS CLOUDS A threat to flying at all levels. They occur when the air is unstable to great heights and that normally means the upper air is more then usually cold. When such a condition occurs with relatively high surface temperatures, the air that rises as thermals is not limited in its ascent before it reaches the tropopause. There, as it cannot penetrate the tropopause, it spreads out to form the characteristic 'anvil' of false cirrus cloud that is the trademark of big shower clouds and thunderstorms.

CUMULUS CLOUDS Individual heap clouds whose height is limited by some form of inversion. They are the visible sign of thermal currents as they develop just downwind of thermal sources. They form at their purest in rmP airmasses, but can appear in winds from many directions (see photograph C.2). They are important to all forms of gliding, because cumulus days are the best for all levels of attainment. The relation between the lapse rates and the temperature of the environment in which the rising air parcels find themselves is shown in fig. 7.2. When they first form, their bases may be at 2000ft or below, but as the day progresses they gradually rise until the base may be as much as 4000ft or more.

Conditions for heap cloud formation can be found in table 7.1 on pp.64-5.

DEEPENING A depression deepens when its central pressure falls with time. The opposite of this is filling.

DEPRESSIONS or LOWS Generally circular disturbances around which the winds blow in an anti-clockwise direction in the northern hemisphere. They will usually have fronts associated with them and, in fact, most of the lows which affect Atlantic Europe start life as wave disturbances in the Polar Front. Between the travelling lows there are ridges of high pressure and sometimes travelling anticyclones. Many apparently minor low pressure areas may appear as whirls of air without fronts. They have a profound effect on the weather and should not be dismissed when they appear on the forecast TV charts.

There are frontless lows which can cause havoc with the local weather. When these come directly from the polar seas they are called Polar Lows. Ones that form over heated land masses are Thermal Lows, but there are others which appear at any time of year as innocuous-looking things, sometimes with just a single isobar round them. They often occupy areas of the chart where the winds are light and so look possible for flying. Possible it may be, but you can never trust the weather for very long in the area of such shallow lows. Never discount the low which lies over your site, despite its lack of fronts. Fronts on TV charts, etc. make lows obvious, but they may not bring the worst anti-flying weather and the lesser kinds can linger for days on end.

Three phases in the development of Polar Front depressions are shown in fig. D.1. On the left, a wave appears in the Polar Front and over its apex the pressure falls. Air moves directly into this new low pressure region, but after less than a day the Earth's rotational effect will have the wind blowing round the centre to obey Buys Ballot's Law. At this stage the centre is some hundreds of miles/kilometres south of the axis of the jet stream and the embryonic low may travel fast along the Polar Front.

After some time the low will deepen and develop while its centre moves north-east

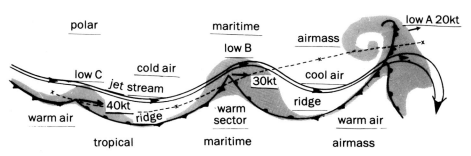

Fig. D.1   Three stages in the development of a depression or maybe three lows of a family along the Polar Front. Low A is occluding and filling-up. Low B is in its prime, while Low C is as yet a wave and may not fully develop. If it does develop, it will go through the stages B and A. Distances and heights are typical values

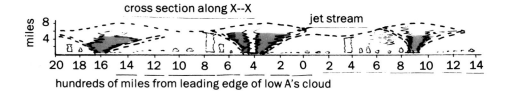

towards the jet axis. The depression is now in its prime and has developed a warm sector. However, the cold front travels faster than the warm front and, when the low centre moves in under the jet, the cold front begins to overtake the warm. The occlusion process then begins. The low now starts to fill; it will eventually fully occlude and disappear due to subsiding air from aloft.

The lower part of fig. D.1 shows a cross-section through the clouds of the three stages, as well as indicating the scale of the typical full-blown depression.

DEWPOINT TEMPERATURE (or THE DEWPOINT) Temperature to which any parcel of air must be reduced before the invisible water vapour in it can condense into cloud or fog. This cooling may occur due to contact with a colder surface, as happens with radiation and advection fog, by ascent along frontal surfaces, by convection currents, or by being pushed up hill and mountain slopes (mechanical lifting). The base of Cu clouds occurs at the level where the ascending thermal air has fallen to the dewpoint. Thus, if the dewpoint is high, the cloud base is low, and vice versa.

The dewpoint becomes closer and closer to the air temperature as the air becomes closer to being saturated with water vapour.

DIURNAL VARIATION Term which includes all of the changes that go on during a normal day. They are all primarily due to the effect of the sun on the ground, so they will apply to any day when the sun manages to shine, even for only part of the time.

The changes are summarised in fig. 6.2 for ground level. The ground temperature does what one would expect and is highest at local noon and lowest at local dawn. The air temperature lags on that by an hour or two, being highest at about 2 p.m. GMT in Britain. It is the thermal currents that the ground induces which control the time when the overnight inversion is broken. This is when the wind picks up for the day and probably veers somewhat at the same time (see table D.1 below). As the thermals punch higher and mix at greater depth, the wind at the surface increases until its speed is maximum at the same time as the air temperature is maximum. After this time the currents can no longer mix the boundary layer so deeply and the wind speed falls slowly until towards late afternoon the inversion sets in. At this time the wind speed will rapidly fall and maybe back somewhat. It will lose much of its gustiness and the airflow of the early evening may tend towards laminar flow. The wind speed tends to fall through the night, but it may pick up locally due to nocturnal wind influences. The diurnal variation in wind speed may be disrupted by changes in the pressure gradient (e.g. coming lows).

It is important to realise that the wind speed at around 1,000ft does exactly the opposite (see fig. 6.4).

TABLE D.1 DATES AND TIMES AT WHICH SUN IS MORE THAN 30° ABOVE THE HORIZON

Latitude	Location	Dates Feb 18 and Oct 25	Mar 21 and Sept 23	Apr 21 and Aug 23	June 22
58N	North Scotland, Skaggerak, North Baltic	Never higher than 20°	1030-1330	0830-1530	0700-1700
52N	Southern Ireland, Central Southern England, Holland	Never higher than 27°	0930-1430	0800-1600	0700-1700
46N	Central Biscay coast of France, North Adriatic	1030-1330	0900-1500	0800-1800	0700-1700
38N	Lisbon, Toe of Italy, Southern Aegean	0930-1430	0830-1530	0800-1600	0700-1700

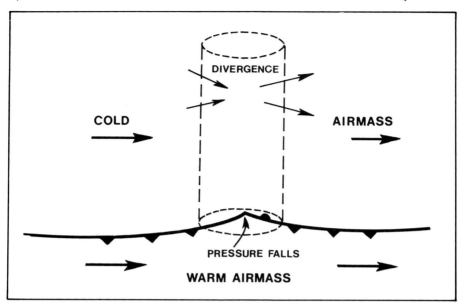

*Fig. D.2 Divergence at altitude allows pressure to fall over the apex of a young depression.
More air flows out of the column than enters it*

DIVERGENCE Met. term indicating that more air is leaving a column than is entering it.
This leads to falling surface pressure and is present when a new depression is being born
and also during the time when a developing low is deepening. It is the opposite of *Convergence* (see fig. D.2).

DOWNWIND Means flying with the wind. Normally, you do not expect to come back to
where you started. It also means in the direction in which the wind is going, i.e. for west
wind, downwind is east.

ELR – ENVIRONMENTAL LAPSE RATE Way in which the air changes its temperature with height as recorded by radiosonde ascents (see *Tephigram*).

EVAPORATION Process by which liquid turns into vapour. In the process latent heat
has to be taken in and so cooling results. Here we are only interested in water or ice. Clouds
will evaporate when their surroundings warm up, as happens when they are caught in
subsiding air or they are part of an airstream that is descending a mountain slope. They can
evaporate if they are not supplied with enough moisture to maintain them. The trailing
edges of lenticularis clouds are formed by the wave shape of the descending air there (see
fig. C.2).

Water on surfaces evaporates more rapidly if:

(1) its temperature increases, e.g. the sun comes out, and

(2) dryer air comes along, e.g. the wind begins to blow.

Both methods are combined in windscreen demisters (see also *Condensation*).

FACSIMILE Weather facsimile is the means by which you can receive the most up-to-
date weather charts, both actual and forecast. You need the necessary receiving equipment
which has to include a stable radio receiver with side band facility, a decoder and a printer.
Models exist for use with a computer.

The best station for Europe is Offenbach One which gives an almost 24-hour output, including actual and forecast charts for surface and upper air plus some simple charts for use by the media. There is a sequence of forecast charts carrying you forwards for the next six days, enabling you to get an idea of what lies in store and to do some forward planning. Another useful set are the charts which show the computer predictions of rainfall areas and amounts for three days ahead and, in winter, the depth of snow lying across the Alps, etc. Various weather charts in this book are based on fax originals.

FALLSTREAKS These are the 'tails' that sink back under cirrus clouds. They are actually showers of ice crystals falling out of the base of denser cirrus heads. The cirrus ahead of coming bad weather has a characteristic 'hooked' appearance and this is due to the strong change of wind with height at cirrus levels. The more rapidly the fallstreaks stream back below the cirrus heads, the greater this 'wind shear' and so the stronger the jet with which it is associated. When the upper air is particularly 'wet' the individual fallstreaks from many cirrus cloud elements combine to form dense white banners stretching across the sky, often from horizon to horizon. Such banners are also associated with jet streams (see photograph 1).

FINE Literally means 'no cloud', so nothing but sunshine by day and clear skies at night.

FLOCCUS Form of altocumulus associated with instability at its level and often precedes the arrival of thunderstorms. It is often seen with castellanus (see photograph F.1).

F.1 Sometimes floccus appears in an otherwise clear sky. It may not in this case mean the later onset of thunder, but the situation needs monitoring

FOG The most unpredictable element in weather forecasting. You will only ever get a vague forecast of where and when fog will form. When fog is mentioned as a possibility for your area, take heed, especially if going high to find a suitable site. Fog is often possible at altitude when it is clear at lower levels. This will generally be upslope fog which forms when wet air is blown up the slopes. It will be most likely over the tops in the lift band and can form suddenly for no apparent reason.

The word 'fog' in aviation forecasts means that the visibility is likely to fall below a kilometre. Mist or smoke haze are forecast when the visibility is likely to lie between 1 and 2km. However, the limits for domestic forecasts are much more stringent, as they are mainly aimed at road users. Here, dense fog will mean a visibility of less than 50 yds/metres. Fog means less than 200 yds while mist means 200 yds to 1,100 yds, i.e. 1km.

Other forms of fog are covered in chapter 13.

FÖHN WINDS Dangerous winds which blow on the Alpine Foreland. They appear when gradient winds are routed over the barrier of the Alps from the Mediterranean. The mountain barrier literally dams up the airflow until it bursts through the mountain passes and falls as a dry, unnervingly warm wind down through the valleys. While Föhn may be strong to gale, it is often not as strong as that, but its most important factor may be the well-known psychological one which makes people more prone to accidents before and during its period of activity. Any substantial mountain barrier can produce echoes of the Föhn effect and it is known on the Scottish east coast in the neighbourhood of Aberdeen and also on the lee side of the Pennines when winds blow from easterly points.

FRONTS Surfaces of transition between one airmass and another of different characteristics. The process of frontal formation is called frontogenesis and occurs when, for example, a cold wet airmass (mP) meets a warm wet airmass (mT) (the process is shown in fig. F.1(a)). However, the two airmasses cannot remain like this for very long. The cold, dense mP air must undercut the lighter mT air, so producing a sloping frontal surface. This serves to lower the centre of mass (G) of the whole system, thereby injecting a massive amount of gravitational energy into the system, which transforms into cloud, wind and precipitation.

Because of this undercutting of the warm air by the cold, warm fronts slope forwards in the direction of travel while cold fronts slope backwards. From a practical point of view this means that warm fronts (and the warm front parts of occlusions) give hours of warning of their approach while cold fronts creep up on you, often unannounced.

The angle of slope of cold fronts is about twice that of warm fronts and so they tend to pass twice as quickly. However, there are many stages in the growth and decay of cold fronts and where they are in the process of decay (frontolysis) they may produce cloud and even drizzle ahead of the front line proper.

The characteristics of fronts are modified by the terrain they have to traverse, especially at the surface, and so it may be that when a warm or a cold front pass there seems to be very little difference between one type of air and the other. It is only in the upper air that the forecaster, using his tephigrams, can truly detect the discontinuities.

Cloud build-up ahead of warm fronts and the warm front parts of occlusions is covered in chapter 3. It is also a good idea to remember that warm front rain (or snow) starts gently and increases in intensity until the front passes, whereas cold front rain starts heavily and tails away with time. Snow may come in ahead of where the cold front meets the surface and, if the front is occluded, rain from the warm front part can turn to snow under the cold front part. See *Occlusions.*

GEOSTROPHIC WIND Wind measured from the spacing of the isobars on a weather map. The term represents the balance that is struck between the desire of the wind to blow directly from higher to lower pressure down the pressure gradient and the apparent centrifugal force exerted on it by having to move on a rotating Earth. The latter effect provides the geostrophic force (GF) which effectively makes air deflect to the right of its path in the Northern Hemisphere and to the left in the Southern. At a fixed latitude the size of the geostrophic force depends only on the wind speed (V). If, as in fig. G.1 (p.150), the wind is represented by a ball on the inside of a dish, then where the gradient is steep a large

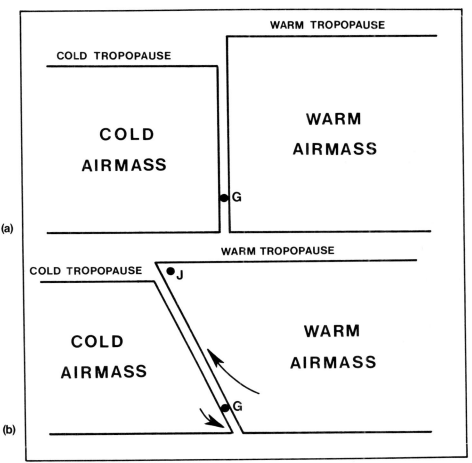

Fig. F.1 Ideally, when two airmasses of different characteristics first come together, their interface is vertical. However, it cannot remain that way and the cold air drives in under the warm while the warm slopes up over the cold. With less cold dense air and more lighter warm air in the column containing the centre of gravity G, the latter will fall, providing energy for the system

opposing GF is needed to balance the pressure gradient force (PG) which is providing the tendency to 'slip down the gradient'. However, that entails a strong wind (as V is bigger if GF is bigger) and so it can be seen that closely spaced isobars and a strong wind go together – you cannot have one without the other.

The strength of the geostrophic wind is measured from the spacing of the isobars on a weather map using a specially designed scale called a geostrophic scale (GS). Any one GS will only be correct for one isobar spacing (say, 4mb) and at one latitude. This follows from the formula:

$$\textbf{PG/air density} = 2\ \omega\ \textbf{V sin } \phi$$

In this formula changes in density can be neglected; ω is the fixed angular velocity of the Earth. By fixing the isobar spacing, the pressure difference in PG has been fixed and only

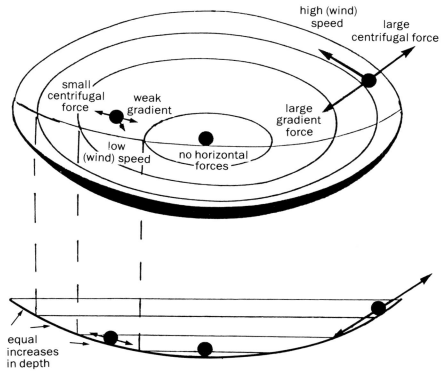

Fig. G.1 An analogy to the balance of Pressure Gradient force (PG) and Geostrophic Force (GF): if a ball runs round the steep part of the dish, it must travel fast so that the centrifugal force balances the gradient force. Where the dish is shallower only a small speed is required to maintain the balance. These are analogous to large wind speed where the isobars are closely packed and low speed where they are widely spaced

the distance apart of the isobars, the wind speed V and the latitude ϕ can vary. The error induced by neglecting changes in latitude over a 10° span is far outweighed by other inherent errors when using a geostrophic scale. So, forget sin ϕ as well, and then we have: distance apart of the isobars (D) x geostrophic wind speed (V) = constant. As D gets smaller, V has to be larger, and vice versa.

The problem is to find the constant, but there is a simple quick way to make a geostrophic scale if you need to. The method is summed up in fig. G.2 which overcomes the fact that a geostrophic scale can only be right for just one map scale.

Get a piece of transparent plastic sheet and mark the distance from the Scilly Isles to North Foreland. If two isobars 4mb apart went through these places, the geostrophic wind (GW) would be 10 knots. Halve the measured distance for 20kt and halve again for 40kt, etc. Double for 5kt. You can use this geostrophic scale on a map of that scale over most of Europe, but in northern latitudes the distance is less and in the Mediterranean it is more. The inset shows you how to alter the scale for different isobar intervals.

While the GW is what is measured, the 'working' wind is the gradient wind. How to use a geostrophic scale is shown in fig. G.3.

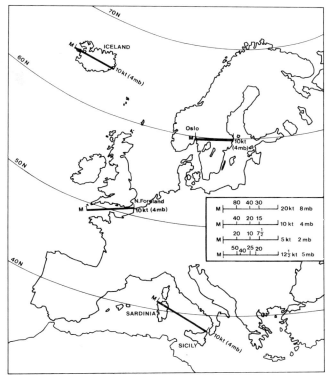

Above *Fig. G.2 You can make a geostrophic scale for any scale of chart across the European theatre by marking off the distance across Iceland at 65N, across Sweden at 60N, across England at 50N and from Sardinia to Sicily at 40N. The inset scales show how to mark off the lengths corresponding to various wind speeds for different spacing of the isobars*

Below *Fig. G.3 At (A) the Geostrophic Scale gives a GW of 20 knots which, because the isobars are not curved, is the same as the gradient wind. At (B) halve the GW where the isobars are highly curved and lower it to 2G/3 further out. At (C) increase the GW where isobars curve anticyclonically*

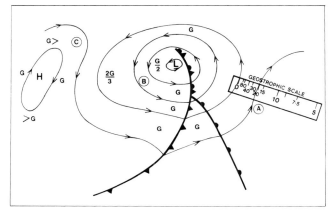

GLIDE ANGLE Angle between the glide path and the horizontal.

GLIDE PATH Flight path of glider.

GLIDE RATIO Horizontal penetration divided by rate of vertical sink. It happens to be the same figure as lift/drag.

GRADIENT This is a term used in different contexts.

(1) The gradient of the isobars is the rate at which the pressure falls (or rises) with distance (see above).

(2) The gradient wind (usually called just *the gradient*) is the geostrophic wind (GW) modified to take account of the fact that when isobars curve strongly in a cyclonic way the true wind is not the GW but as little as half the measured value. Less curvature means that the gradient and the GW become more and more the same and, normally, when they are not too strongly curved, the geostrophic scale also roughly gives the gradient wind speed. Certainly, the difference between them can be neglected in most instances. Conversely, when the isobars curve anticyclonically the gradient is stronger than the GW (see fig. G.3).

(3) The way the wind changes speed near the ground with ascent or descent is called the wind gradient (see chapter 6).

GROUND SPEED Your speed, with respect to the ground below and, except when it is calm, it will always be different from your airspeed. Ground speed will be zero if, for example, you are flying into a 12kt wind with a penetration speed of 12kt. Turn through 180° and your ground speed will suddenly shoot up to 24kt.

As an example of a different situation, if a 10kt wind blows onto a ridge and you wish to fly along the axis of the ridge and so stay in the lift band, you will need to fly at about 14-15kt at 45° to the ridge in order to crab along the lift band (see fig. G.4).

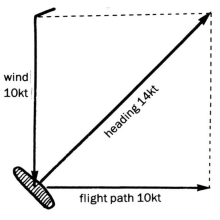

Fig. G.4 To illustrate how a heading at an angle to the wind leads to a flight path across the wind. In this case there is a ground speed of 10 knots sideways

GUSTS AND LULLS Recurrent feature of the wind near the surface on most flying days. They occur especially with the thermal structure that accompanies cumulus. Gusts are parcels of wind brought down from higher up where the wind is stronger. They barge into the slower surface air; therefore, the wind speed rises sharply when a gust strikes. When observed in one spot the wind will usually stay up at its gust speed for maybe a minute or two and then will slowly subside until we are back in the slower surface air which is recognised as a lull. If flying in gusty conditions, remember that you are moving through the gust cells whenever you have penetration speed. You will meet gusts more often flying towards and across the wind and less often flying downwind (see chapter 7).

GUST FACTOR When variable winds change speed by 5 knots or more in a time of 4 seconds or less they are unsafe for flying paraglidgers. It is a rule of thumb that prevents paraglider pilots flying in conditions of dangerous thermal turbulence. The point can be illustrated with reference to fig. 7.7: the gust at 2 minutes well exceeds the gust factor, as does the sudden lull at 3 minutes.

HALOES Formed by refraction in ice crystals at high altitude. The most familiar is the ring halo about the sun, or moon, whose radius just about fits the outstretched hand at arm's length. However, a large number of rare rings, arcs, etc. can be seen on occasions. In all cases they indicate the presence of cirrostratus and therefore the probable onset of the warm front of a depression. Haloes are largely colourless and are not to be confused with coloured iridescences on the edges of alto clouds or coloured patches (sun dogs) on the same level as the sun. Colour indicates water-droplet cloud and so is lower than the Cs cloud associated with haloes.

HAZE Present when the obscuration is largely due to smoke or dust, etc. (i.e. dry particles) and the visibility lies between 1 and 2km.

HEAT or THERMAL LOWS Develop over heated land areas during the middle of the day. They may become the breeding ground for showers or thunderstorms, especially when they are fed with 'fuel' in the shape of cool moist air from the sea. Local winds will blow into heat lows when conditions are otherwise quiet, starting directly into the low centre but veering with time.

HECTOPASCAL SI unit of pressure of one hundred pascals, equivalent to a millibar.

HURRICANES Cyclones which develop over the warm tropical seas of the southern North Atlantic and normally track westwards towards the Caribbean, curving to the right and so emerging on a north-easterly path towards Europe (see fig. H.1). They have usually been demoted to depressions by the time they have crossed the Atlantic, but they have a

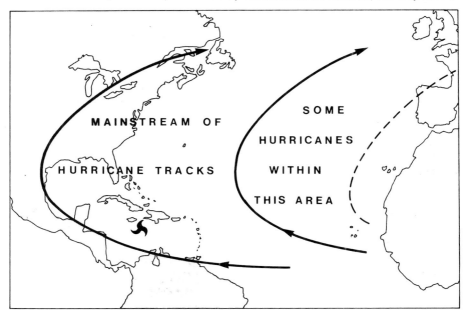

Fig. H.1   The way hurricanes track and the route by which they may re-curve to threaten Atlantic Europe in autumn

nasty habit of rejuvenating themselves and producing some very bad weather in September and October, both in Britain and on the Continent. The major difference in structure between hurricanes and depressions is that the winds rotate the same way from bottom to top in a hurricane, whereas with a depression the lower circulating winds have to unwind into the upper westerlies. This tends to put a brake on the maximum severity of the surface winds of a depression, whereas no such break exists in the hurricane. If an autumn forecast intimates that a coming depression was once a hurricane, expect it to produce some nasty surprises.

HUMIDITY MIXING RATIO (r) Mass in grams of water vapour in a kilogram of dry air. If water vapour is added to the dry air until it is unable to hold any more vapour, then the air is said to be saturated with vapour and the new HMR (R) is that for saturation. The Relative Humidity is the ratio r/R expressed as a percentage. The values of r and R must be found at the same air temperature.

Saturated air must therefore have a relative humidity (RH) of 100%, and the drier the air, the lower the value of the RH. Relative humidity is found using devices called hygrometers. To find the RH accurately is difficult and reliance should not be placed on the cheap dial types of hygrometer which can be purchased from garden centres, etc. If you need to know the RH, you should ask your nearest met. office.

HYDROMETEORS Collective word for everything made of water molecules. These include droplets of cloud, fog and mist, as well as of rain, drizzle, snow, sleet, hail, etc. This differentiates them from such particles as dust, sand and salt from sea spray, smoke, and many kinds of chemicals that are pushed into the atmosphere by industrial processes.

ICING It is to be hoped that no glider pilot will have to contend with icing. Ice accretion on parts of an aircraft will build up in supercooled wet air, i.e. in cloud above freezing level. It could be a hazard if flights are made from very high points and there is cold cloud below. The only other way the glider pilot may meet it is if he flies too closely under a Cb cloud and gets taken up in the updraught. Such an encounter could be fatal.

IMPERIAL UNITS Despite various moves to replace feet by metres, miles by kilometres, etc. it is often found useful to retain imperial units. An example is that, for aviation purposes, height is given in thousands of feet, despite the meteorological height unit being geopotential metres. The following are some useful conversions:

    1 foot (ft) = 0.305 metres (m)
    1 pound (lb) = 453.6 grams (g)
    1 mile (mi) = 1.6 kilometres (km)
    1 horsepower (hp) = 746 watts (W).

INTERMITTENT RAIN Rain that is not continuous over a considerable period, but the periods of precipitation are of substantial duration and the sky remains overcast.

INVERSIONS Layers of relatively warm air overlaying colder air. This situation produces stability in that the air in the inversion layer tends to sink, following a universal rule for fluids at different temperatures which states that 'Heat seeks cold', i.e. air that is warm will try to move towards air that is cooler. The rule applies, for example, to thermals where heated parcels of air move upwards, seeking cooler regions above. This is an unstable situation. An inversion, on the other hand, is a stable situation and will put a lid on convection currents and will effectively separate winds above the inversion from those below it (see fig. 5.5). Because of this, as explained under *Mixing*, the formation of inversions lowers the speed of winds below them, which is why the surface wind goes down with evening but comes up again in the morning (see *Diurnal variation*).

There are many reasons for inversions forming, but when clouds have limited tops the reason will almost always be that some kind of inversion exists around the level of the cloud tops. An inversion will form during most nights, starting near the ground and extending higher with time. Stratocumulus cloud may develop in this overnight inversion, but should disperse when the sun gets to work on it in summer. Other inversions are due to the release of latent heat aloft by Cb clouds when they condense their water vapour into cloud and precipitation. This inversion is the one which limits the growth of fair weather cumulus in rmP airstreams (see *Airmasses*).

The effect of the overnight inversion on wind speed is evident in fig. 6.4. If using mechanical lift over a ridge in the late afternoon or early evening, you must allow for the wind speed aloft being greater than might otherwise be expected from its strength at take-off.

ISOBARS Lines joining places with equal atmospheric pressure. They may be drawn at 2, 4, 5 or 8 millibar intervals. It is usual for those shown on British TV to be drawn at 4mb intervals, but they may be 5mb in Europe and are sometimes 8mb on newspaper charts.

KATABATICS Winds that sink off hill and mountain slopes in quiet weather. They set in when the sun deserts the higher reaches and thus are mainly light breezes of late afternoon and through the night. When aided by land breezes they become nocturnal winds. When aided by down-slope winds from high snow-topped mountains they can blow fresh to gale.

KELVIN SCALE Scientifically based scale of temperature with which the Celsius scale agrees in degree size. However, it is found that there is an Absolute Zero of temperature which is 273 degrees below the freezing point of water. No substance can have a temperature lower than Absolute Zero and this is the zero of the Kelvin (K) scale. Thus the freezing point of water is 273K and the boiling point, 373K.

KNOT (kt) A nautical mile per hour and the meteorological unit of wind speed. The nautical mile is 6080ft or 1.85km. The following are conversion factors from knots into other speed units.

1 knot = 0.51 m/s = 1.15 mph = 1.85 km/h. For practical purposes 1 m/s = 2 kt.

LAND BREEZES Opposite of seabreezes and blow during the nights of quiet weather from land to sea. They are at their strongest when the contrast in temperature between the sea and the land is most marked. This means that they are most likely in early autumn, but when aided by katabatics off coast-wise hills they can appear at many times of the year. When aided by down-slope winds from snow-capped mountains, they can become strong and last well into the morning over coastal cliff sites (see fig. 10.3).

LAPSE RATES Amount by which the temperature of air parcels falls as they ascend. The Dry Adiabatic Lapse Rate (DALR) is 3°C per 1000ft of ascent and applies to all air that is not saturated. Once saturated, further cooling by ascent means that condensation has to occur. This releases latent heat, which slows the rate of cooling by half, i.e. 1.5°C/1000ft. This is called the Wet Adiabatic Lapse Rate (WALR). It must not be forgotten that air parcels also warm at these rates when they descend (see also *ELR*).

LATENT HEAT Heat which apparently lies dormant or hidden (hence latent) in vapours, but which becomes released when the vapour condenses into liquid: molecules of vapour are much more energetic than when they are constrained in the liquid state, and they must release the difference when they condense. The amounts of heat involved in weather processes is vast. If a centimetre depth of rain falls over an area of a square metre, then somewhere in the clouds over 22 Megajoules of heat will have been released as the water vapour formed the rain drops.

As there are tons of water in the clouds of fronts, so one of the major ways in which upper levels are warmed is by the production of clouds. Such release of heat at altitude eventually inhibits the upward growth of clouds by forming a temperature inversion.

Conversely, when water evaporates into vapour, latent heat is taken in and the surroundings must cool. So, if the same centimetre of water as in the example above should evaporate, the same 22 Megajoules of heat have now to be given to the water to supply the energy to emit the molecules from its surfaces. Thus, when the dew evaporates in the morning, heat (which otherwise would go to raise the air temperature) is taken in, but of course the relative humidity remains high while the process goes on. Only when wind mixes the wet air near the surface with drier air high up does the RH fall markedly.

A similar but much smaller quantity of latent heat is involved when ice melts into water. Snow melting keeps the air temperature down while the formation of ice on the surface of a pond, etc. demands the release of latent heat as its molecules become suddenly immobile after having been quite mobile in the water state.

LENTICULAR CLOUDS Occur mainly as altocumulus lenticularis (Ac lent) and mark the wave crests when a mountain barrier induces wave streaming into a stable airstream. There are also associated cirrocumulus lenticularis (Cc lent) at high altitude, while sometimes stratocumulus lenticularis (Sc lent) is found at lower levels. They are popularly known amongst pilots as 'lenties', being a very important sign of possible danger from rotors and other wave-induced turbulence (see photographs 5 and 9).

LIFT BAND Roughly sausage-shaped volume of air over a windward slope up which dynamic lift is occurring (see fig. 8.3).

LIFT TO DRAG RATIO (L/D) See *Glide ratio*.

LIGHTNING Result of electric charge of opposite sign being built up in different parts of cumulonimbus clouds and in the Earth or sea below. They are indeed giant electric sparks either from ground to cloud (ground strokes) or from cloud to cloud (cloud strokes) (see fig. L.1). As the charge centres are found to lie between temperature levels of -10°C to -25°C, so only deep Cb clouds can generate thunder in summer. It is not exactly known how the immense voltages (sometimes as high as a thousand million volts) are generated.

When cloud strokes are involved (as they frequently are with unstable fronts), so-called 'sheet' lightning occurs. This is, however, only the reflection of forked lightning off cloud elements. It explains the old belief that sheet lightning is not dangerous, although there is, in fact, no such thing as lightning that occurs in sheets rather than in branching forks.

The first lightning stroke appears about 10-20 minutes after the start of any sizeable rain from a thunderstorm cell, but as cells are being born continuously during a thunderstorm lightning occurs more or less continually in different places at different times, leading to the idea that lightning never strikes the same place twice.

'Summer lightning' seen at night is too far away for the accompanying thunder to be heard. As the range of thunder is typically 10-15 miles, such lightning indicates a distant storm. The rule for finding the distance of a flash is to count the number of seconds between seeing the flash and hearing the thunder and to divide by 5. The answer is in miles. Divide by 3 for kilometres.

LIGHTNING CONDUCTORS Grounded metal pointed objects designed either to discharge a potential lightning strike or to conduct it harmlessly to earth if it occurs. As in fig. L.1, the effect of the point is to create an 'electric wind' of ions whose sign is the opposite of that in the lower reaches of the cloud above. This ionic 'wind' may be sufficient to prevent a strike when the build-up of potential in the cloud is not very rapid. If it is very fast and the electric wind cannot sufficiently neutralise it, the 'wind' provides an ionised path to steer the stroke to the conductor.

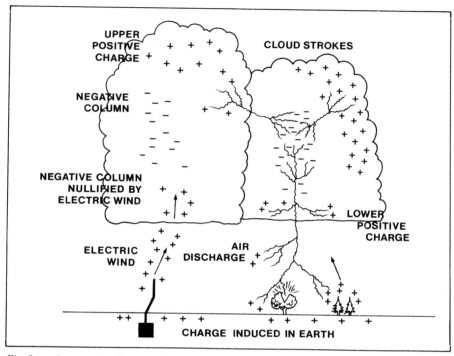

Fig. L.1 A composite diagram showing on the left the possible effect of an electric wind from a grounded point and on the right cloud strokes and ground strokes. Conifers produce an electric wind and so are less often struck than broad-leaved trees

Because grouped conifers are rarely, if ever, struck, it is thought that the combined point action of their needles creates enough electric wind to neutralise all but the most vociferous thunderstorms. Broad-leafed trees, and especially oaks, on the other hand, are prone to strikes and you should never shelter under them, particularly if they are isolated.

LINE SQUALLS Accompaniment to ana cold fronts. Lines of low black cloud are associated with a sharp rise in wind speed and an equally sharp wind veer. The barometer kicks up, temperature falls and thunder may be heard. They do not last long, but they can wreak havoc with unsecured gliders.

MAMMATOFORM CLOUDS Inverted dome-shaped cloud masses that form on the edges of cumulonimbus clouds. Once a good example of mamma is seen, it is not easily forgotten. Mamma may be seen at the leading edge of Cb clouds, but more often they are seen when the storm clouds are retreating. However, in the United States the sight of mamma is associated with the risk of tornadoes and the same may be the case in Europe where, although they are less vicious than in the US, they occur more often than is usually thought (see photograph M.1).

MEDITERRANEAN WEATHER Not as benign as the holiday brochures would have you believe. Certainly, a semi-permanent anticyclone settles over the south-eastern half of the area most summers and extends its influence to the majority of the coastal regions south of the mountain barriers. However, that does not prevent the region having massive thunderstorms, suffering from waterspouts and tornadoes and, in many places, having a much stronger wind regime than in the rest of Europe.

M.1 Descending air in the rear of a passing thunderstorm cell lead to mammatoform clouds

In the second and third weeks in October most years the so-called 'autumn break' moves across the Mediterranean, starting in the west and gradually shifting places further east towards the cool season regime. It is important to check the climate of a place you intend to visit and to find out what it is like, say, early morning, as well as the expected maximum temperature in the middle of the day. Also, try to discover what, how and where local winds blow (see below).

MEDITERRANEAN WINDS The Mediterranean is dominated by regional winds. Winds due to pressure systems invade the area through the Gironde and other gaps in the mountain barriers. These also induce the massive mountain-gap winds such as the Mistral, the Bora and the Tramontana when the isobars are routed for gradient winds from the north and north-east. The mild, wet winters are very windy and the worst area is the Gulf of Lions, but gale-force winds occur sometime, somewhere in any season. Winds from the south tend to be hot, dry and dust-laden, while others will try to follow the waterways such as the Adriatic and the Aegean. The following are some of the attributes of the regional winds (see fig. M.1).

Names and regions	Characteristics	Season, place, time, etc.
Mistral (Mistraou, Maistre, Magistral, etc.)	Cold, dry and often strong. Sometimes viciously squally.	See Mistral below.
Maestrale	Often brings fair or fine weather; usually no rain, snow, etc.	The Mistral that has lost its bite across Sardinia and Tyrrhenian Sea.
Bora	Cold, strong outflow from NE into Adriatic through the Trieste Gap and over mountains of Yugoslavia.	Most frequent mid-winter. Can extend to whole of the Med. Even in summer Bora produces unexpected gales.

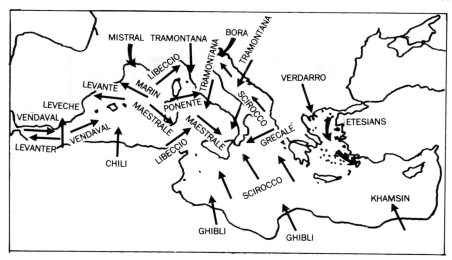

Fig. M.1 The major regional winds of the Mediterranean. Some of these are given local names in different places

Tramontana	Bora flowing over and off the Appenines. Dry and clear. Often cloudless.	Extends to Corsica and Sardinia as well as Sicily.
Grecale	The Tramontana when it comes from Greece.	
Verdarro	The cool north wind from the Balkans into the Aegean.	Feeds into the largely N winds of the Aegean.
Etesians (Meltemi in Turkey)	The 'annuals' of the Aegean which blow regularly from N in the summer. Can extend to whole Med.	NW on the corner of Turkey near Rhodes.
Levante	Long-fetch winds blowing towards Spain. NE wind with squalls and bad weather. May have once been Bora.	Mainly autumn to spring when there are Levante gales.
Levanter	The E wind of the Alboran Channel. Heavy rain, low cloud, poor visibility. Violent squalls and thunderstorms in winter.	All year – but most likely in the cool season.
Vendaval	The W wind of the Alboran Channel extending to the Balearics.	As above.
Leveche	SE to SW dry, dust-laden winds into SE Spain. When extend to north become Marin.	Late spring, early summer. May be as frequent as Mistral.

Names and regions	*Characteristics*	*Season, place, time, etc.*
Chili, Ghibl, Scirroco, Khamsin	Winds from desert areas of North Africa. Very humid, sometimes with fog and low cloud. Produce extreme heat in summer. Occasionally gale force when bad dust storms.	Scirroco may average 5 days a month. Can raise temperature to over 100°F (38°C).
Libeccio	W or SW wind of Italian sea areas. Very hot and dry squalls in summer.	Common to west Italy all year.
Ponente	Originally Mistral through the Strait of Bonnifaccio onto Italian coast.	

METEORS Term for particles in the air which may be solid or liquid and, in some instances, as small as molecules.

MILLIBAR (mb) Standard unit of pressure for met. purposes and a thousandth part of a bar. The latter is 100000 pascals (Pa) and is a useful unit, as standard pressure is close to a bar, being 1013.24mb. Normally, surface atmospheric pressure does not vary outside the limits 50mb above and below a bar. As inches of mercury are still in use, here is a conversion table.

mb	950	960	970	980	990	1000	1010	1020	1030	1040	1050
in.	28.05	28.35	28.64	28.94	29.23	29.53	29.83	30.12	30.42	30.71	31.01

MIRAGES Due to refraction of light near the Earth's surface. The most familiar is the 'wet road' effect seen when a thin layer of air over the surface of a highway is heated to well above normal air temperature. Light from the sky then suffers sufficient refraction to be directed back to the observer. As a layer of water on the road would produce the same refractive effect and the latter is much more familiar, so the hot road surface looks wet.

Heated air layers produce inferior mirage effects, as described above, while cool layers induce superior mirages. The latter can be seen from the beach in summer when a distant coastline appears raised above the horizon, whereas under normal circumstances the coast would be just below the horizon and therefore not visible.

MIST Present when the obscuration is due mainly to water droplets and the visibility lies between 1 and 2km.

MISTRAL The masterful down–slope wind of the Rhône valley. Similar winds with local names blow off the mountains inland all the way from the Spanish-French border to Genoa (see pages 82–3).

MIXING A most important concept when attempting to understand the behaviour of the wind near the Earth's surface. It is covered in detail in chapter 4. The depth of the lower atmosphere that is mixed by turbulent eddies as well as thermals is called the Earth's boundary layer by analogy with the boundary layer over an aerofoil or other aerodynamic structure.

MSL (MEAN SEA LEVEL) Datum for surface pressure and so the datum for QNH.

MULTIPLE FRONTS Although the actual and forecast maps on TV may show fronts as single lines, these are often simplified versions of the true structure which can be complex. In particular, cold fronts may sometimes be several frontal lines, one behind the other as the cold air gradually replaces the warm air. Thus if it appears that a cold front has

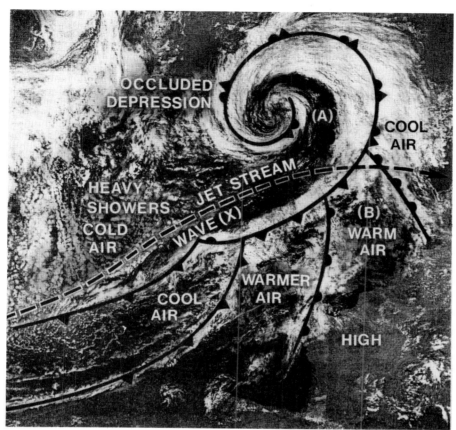

Fig. M.2 A satellite cloud picture to illustrate multiple fronts. Which is which can be sorted out by remembering that the air behind the front gives its name to the front. The trailing cold front from Low A has waves at X and will travel along the front to become lost in the circulation of A

passed but the wind does not veer markedly nor the upper cloud fully clear, it is advisable to delay take-off to see if this really is the clearance or whether another minor frontal line is following (see fig. M.2).

NEPHANALYSIS Interpretation of a satellite cloud image by an expert, giving the cloud types, their amount and distribution. For many people (including meteorologists) a nephanalysis is essential in interpreting the clouds depicted.

NIMBUS Means 'rain-bearing' and so stratus-type cloud that produces rain is called nimbostratus (Ns), while cumulus-type cloud that showers is called cumulonimbus (Cb) (*not* nimbocumulus!) However, not all stratus cloud that rains will be nimbostratus. The latter has to be deep, i.e. upper reaches above the −13°C isotherm, while upslope cloud need not be anywhere near as deep as that for rain to occur (see *Rain*).

NOCTURNAL WINDS Near the coasts the night wind of quiet weather is partly katabatic drift and partly land breeze; together they are termed a nocturnal wind. Inland, beyond the throw of the land breeze, any night wind that starts after evening calm is likely to be due to katabatic drift (see page 99).

OBSERVATIONS Made just before the hour at weather-observing stations throughout the world. They are sent by landline and radio to central collecting stations where computerised systems plot them automatically onto synoptic charts. These, together with the information on upper temperature and humidity, etc. from radiosondes, form the basic information on which the computers produce their actual and forecast charts, both surface and upper air. All this information can be exchanged across the world by cable and satellite, and this obviates a duplication of effort (see *Station circles*).

OCCLUSIONS Occur because the warm front of a depression only travels at two-thirds of the speed of its cold front. Thus during the depression's life cycle (see chapter 3) the cold front gradually overtakes the warm front and either undercuts the latter (cold occlusion) or is undercut by the warm front (warm occlusion). The warm occlusion process occurs when the cold air behind the cold front is actually warmer than that ahead of the warm front (see fig. O.1).

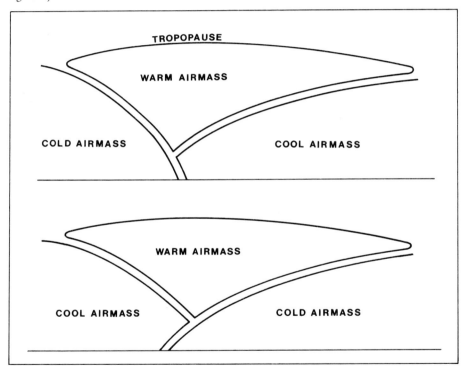

Fig. O.1 The two kinds of occlusion. At the top is a cold occlusion when the air in the rear is colder than the air ahead. At the bottom is a warm occlusion, because cool air is warmer than cold air. Both lift the warm air off the ground altogether

OROGRAPHIC LOWS or LEE DEPRESSIONS Form on the lee sides of mountain ranges such as the Alps. These ranges are high enough to disrupt the normal flow of air over them and the lows form as a consquence.

PANNUS Met. term for fractostratus that forms in the moist air below cloud bases which are beginning to rain. The correct term is stratus pannus or St pan (see photograph P.1).

PASCAL SI (metric) unit of pressure, equivalent to a force of 1 newton(N) acting over a

P.1 Pannus in the early stages of formation. It has often not started to rain at the surface, but must be raining lightly aloft. Expect rain any moment

surface of 1 square metre in area. The newton is quite a small force, e.g. a kilogram of sugar only weighs 10N. Thus atmospheric pressure must be a large number of pascals and lies around 100000 Pa. The millibar is 100 Pa.

PAST WEATHER Plotted south-east of the station circles on a weather map. It covers the last 6 hours at the main synoptic hours of 0600, 1200, 1800 and 0000 GMT and the last 3 hours on the intermediate charts for 0300, 0900, 1500 and 2100. Weather in the past hour also appears in the present weather position on station circles.

PILE OF PLATES Spectacular form of wave cloud which occurs because of differing layers of high and low humidity. They are more prevalent in France than in Britain; the one illustrated in photograph P.2 on p.164 was downwind of the Paps of Jura.

PILEUS Eyebrow-shaped cap of cloud which appears over the heads of rapidly growing cumulus clouds (see fig. 11.1).

POLAR FRONT More or less continuous line of division between polar and tropical airmasses that encircles the temperate latitudes of both hemispheres. It is where most depressions are born.

POLAR LOWS Frontless whirls of air that come down from northern seas, usually on the edges of anticyclones, that are quasi-stationary to the east. They are normally filled with cold, wet air and produce some of the most abysmal weather. They can be slow-moving and take days to clear.

POTENTIAL INSTABILITY Sometimes an airstream is stable at low level, but can be made unstable by being pushed up a hill or mountain side. Thus the low-level airstream is potentially unstable. Such airstreams are also potentially dangerous, because the weather at a gliding site may be much worse than it appears at low level.

PRECIPITATION Collective noun for all the various types of water-based substances that fall from clouds, including rain, drizzle, snow, hail and sleet.

P.2 Sometimes streaming over mountains leads to the spectacular orographic formations called 'A pile of plates'. This 'pile' was over Islay, one of the Western Isles of Scotland, and was probably due to the Paps of Jura

PRESENT WEATHER Plotted west of the station circles on weather maps. The symbols used are international and are based on the following:

• = rain; ⁹ = drizzle, ✱ = snow, △ = hail; ▽ = shower, $\bar{\zeta}$ = thunderstorm; ▽ = squall, = = mist, ≡ = fog. Heavier precipitation is indicated by increasing the number of symbols (up to four), and types of precipitation, with showers and thunderstorms, by plotting the symbol for rain, hail, etc. over that for the shower or storm. A shortened version of the present weather code is to be found in *Meteorology and Flight* by Tom Bradbury (A & C Black).

PRESSURE Force exerted on unit area; specifically for met. purposes it is the force exerted by the weight of the atmosphere. It acts equally in all directions and is basically due to the constant bombardment of the surface by immense numbers of molecules of air and water vapour. Pressure increases when:

(1) the number of molecules increases – which means that the density of the air increases

(2) the average speed of the molecules increases – which means that the temperature of the air increases.

However, the process is complicated by convergence and divergence aloft. So, pressure may fall due to divergence in the air column above the site, or to the arrival of less dense air over the site, or to both things happening together (see also chapter 1 and *Pascal*).

PRESSURE GRADIENT See *Geostrophic wind* and *Gradient wind*.

PROGNOSIS Met. term for forecasts.

Q-CODE Abbreviated code for wireless telegraph (W/T) messages, but the terms are used now in their own right. The ones most likely to be encountered by the glider pilot are:

QFE = take off or landing site pressure

QFF = sea level pressure
QNH = altimeter setting.

QUASI-STATIONARY Term used to describe the mainly slight motions of cyclonic and anticyclonic centres when the latter are not, as a whole, moving much. No pressure centre is ever static for very long and it may rearrange itself from day to day, becoming possibly complex with time until it eventually moves on or disappears.

RADAR Increasingly being used for local short-term weather forecasting. The ability to 'see' rain, especially heavy rain, combined with the pictures from geostationary satellites, provides instant weather warnings of sudden deluges, the outbreak of heavy thunderstorms, etc. Some of this intelligence is broadcast during TV metcasts, but when you want the information at any other time you must obtain it from another met. facility, such as a weather shop. It is unlikely that the majority of airfields will be in receipt of the information. When very heavy showers or thunderstorms are possible, in which flooding or structural damage may be caused, a severe-weather warning is broadcast via national and local radio networks (see fig. R.1).

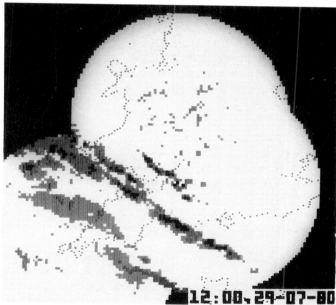

Fig. R.1 A radar image of showery troughs advancing north-eastwards across Southwest and Southern England and Wales. The bulbous lobe shape of the picture reflects the limit of the radar coverage

RADIATION FOG Fog which forms over land on clear nights.

RADIOSONDES Sent aloft twice a day at 0000 and 1200 GMT to sample pressure temperature and humidity. The information is sent back as coded radio signals and a good 'ascent' may take the balloon to over 80,000ft. The balloons are followed by radar to gauge the upper winds. Simple balloon ascents with radar reflectors are sent up at 0600 and 1800 so that the upper winds can be more closely monitored.

RAIN Normally starts off as snow in the higher reaches of deep clouds. The chances of enough individual water molecules meeting and staying together to form the nucleus of a rain drop is so small as to be negligible. Therefore, some other mechanism must be at work.

Individual ice crystals form in clouds whose tops have fallen below about -13°C. They do so by water molecules 'freezing' onto so-called condensation nuclei which may be other ice crystals, sea salt from breaking waves, dust particles and chemicals, etc. These ice crystals form into snow flakes which fall gently into warmer regions and, in so doing, melt into rain drops. All large rain drops form this way, but the very big 'thunderspots' associated with electric storms also need to be electrically charged. The 'parachute' effect with snowflakes allows descent to a low enough level for air friction not to disrupt the drops greatly as they melt, thus preventing them splitting into smaller drops. The effect of charging drops electrically is to maintain their cohesion and allow those that would otherwise break up to survive to the surface. Thus when thunder spots splosh onto the windscreen it indicates a state of electrification in the clouds overhead. This may not necessarily lead to lightning.

Most rain, therefore, falls from nimbostratus (frontal) or cumulonimbus (frontal and convective) clouds, as these two types are the ones which develop sufficiently deeply. Most rain in the winter is from Ns and most in the summer from Cb clouds. However, alto clouds can also rain, especially when they become unstable, leading to high-level showers which may be thundery, although they may not necessarily develop enough to create lightning.

Rain can also occur from 'warm' clouds, particularly in the tropics, but the process is then one of growth by collision. Neither large raindrops nor heavy rain can be induced by droplets colliding with one another and coalescing. However, coalescence is the way drizzle is formed and in met. terms drizzle has a droplet size of less than half a millimetre (0.04in.) in diameter, while rain is larger than this. Thus drizzle is a 'warm' cloud phenomenon.

RAINBOWS Due to the refraction of sunlight through falling rain drops. The way in which the light is internally reflected within the drop is shown in fig. R.2.

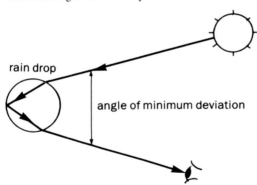

rain drop

angle of minimum deviation

Fig. R.2 How light from the sun gets to the eye through a raindrop. At the angle of minimum deviation for a given colour that colour is seen brightly

A rainbow indicates that rain is falling to leeward. The windward sky may suggest that the rain has passed or it may indicate that a dry period is about to be invaded by showers.

RAIN SHADOWS Appear on the sides of mountain and hill ranges away from the prevailing wind. Such areas are also prone to wave-streaming problems.

RELATIVE WIND Apparent wind with respect to the glider. This is different from the real wind, as the glider is always falling through at the same time as penetrating the air.

RETURNING MARITIME POLAR AIR (rmP) One of the chief airmasses in which fair-weather cumulus form. It has a long history of passage over the deep Atlantic round the semi-permanent Icelandic Low.

RIDGES Ridges of high pressure stick out from anticyclones. In the Atlantic European theatre the most prominent and persistent one is that which extends up from the Azores anticyclone. Ridges are regions of dry but not necessarily good flying weather, often being extensively cloudy. See *Airmasses*.

RIME Icing is opaque, white build-up that occurs on solid surfaces when freezing fog or cloud blows by.

ROTORS Regions of extremely dangerous turbulence which occur in association with strong wind forms of wave streaming.

SATELLITES Those used for met. purposes are of two kinds: polar orbiting and geo-stationary (see fig. S.1). Satellites in geostationary orbit (GSO) are spread round the equator at the 22,000-mile (35,786km) height at which any body orbits at the same angular speed as the Earth. Six such satellites cover the entire globe and, at the time of writing, the one which produces images for Europe is Meteosat 2. It sits over the equator on the Greenwich Meridian and this produces a full-Earth picture every half an hour. These are put together to form the moving sequences seen on some TV metcasts. The Americas have two GSO satellites, GOES East and GOES West, the former being over the Amazon basin and playing a vital role in hurricane tracking (GOES is an acronym for Geostationary Orbiting Environmental Satellite). The latter covers the western Pacific and the China Sea. The final satellite, GOMS (Geostationary Orbiting Meteorological Satellite) looks for cyclones in the Indian Ocean.

The polar orbiters are TIROS (Television Infra-Red Orbiting Satellite) type satellites. How they effectively cover the Earth's surface is evident from fig. S.1. They are much lower in the sky than GSO satellites (about 500 miles/900km) and each orbit takes 101 minutes to complete. The current TIROS satellites are the NOAA (National Oceanic and Atmospheric Administration) series put up by the USA and the Meteor series put up by the former USSR. The NOAA satellites take images both in the visible and infra-red parts of the spectrum, the latter allowing clouds, etc. to be seen overnight. However, the Meteors do not have the infra-red facility. The pictures can be acquired by anyone with APT (Automatic Picture Transmission) equipment on ordinary non-directional dipole aerials.

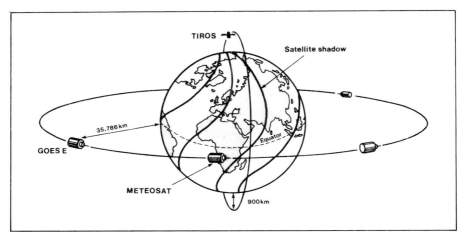

Fig. S.1 The two kinds of weather satellite orbit. The geostationary orbit is the same for all such satellites and must lie over the equator. The TIROS satellites make much lower orbits over the poles and, combined with the Earth's rotation, make a spiral shadow over the Earth

SATURATED ADIABATIC LAPSE RATE (SALR) See *Lapse rates* and chapter 7.

SCUD Another name for fracto-stratus when the latter is formed below lines of frontal passage. It indicates the imminent clearance of a front.

SEABREEZES Coastal winds generated by the land heating to a sufficient temperature above that of the adjacent sea. They set in during the mornings of quiet weather and may move as much as 50 miles (80km) inland during the day. They are covered in chapter 9.

SECONDARY DEPRESSIONS Occur from the growth of waves on the trailing cold fronts of primary depressions. On their polar sides they may lower the wind speed, but on their equatorial sides the gradient is squeezed by the insertion of lower pressure into an already low pressure area. The result is that stronger gales than maybe were produced with the primary depression now occur.

When the cold front of a depression has passed, the showers which ought to continue for a while may die away. There may still be a great deal of Cu about, but it could spread out into Sc with time. If this is coupled to a lightening and backing wind, then expect a secondary depression to be on its way and allow accordingly. See *Crossed winds' rules*.

SEVERE WEATHER WARNINGS Broadcast when a meteorological event is likely to result in damage to life or property. The radar weather watch enables forecasters to give 'now-casts' of very heavy showers or cloudbursts from thunderstorms, etc. These will be broadcast on local radio. Other examples include very strong winds or exceptionally high tides.

SHOWERS Should technically occur from individual Cb clouds with spaces between, but modern forecasts for the public use the term for any situation where the rain is likely to be anything other than continuous. Thus the rainfall from nimbostratus that becomes unstable might be described as 'showers', even though there is 8/8 low cloud cover. Intermittent rain is unlikely to be described as such to avoid confusion.

In any case the clouds must rise above the -13°C isotherm. The process described under rain occurs in their upper reaches. Only deep convection clouds or unstable medium-level clouds will produce true showers.

Much of the so-called continuous rain experienced has a showery nature: it rarely rains steadily, but heavier bursts appear amongst the lighter ones. These are due to local high-level instability zones which are set off amongst the nimbostratus layers. Their correct name is mesoscale precipitation areas (MPAs). Showers are discussed in chapters 3 and 11.

SI (Système Internationale) A scientific, self-consistent set of units and dimensions based on the metre, kilogram, second and ampere as basic units. It is also known as the MKSA system from these unit names and, more loosely, as the Metric system.

In the SI system all unit names which are based on names of people have small initial letters when they are are written fully, but they are given capital letters when abbreviated, e.g. the unit of energy or work done is the joule (J), that of power is the watt (W) and that of pressure is the pascal (Pa). All other units have small letters, e.g. metre (m), kilogram (kg) and second (s).

Pressure is force per unit area and the SI force unit is the newton (N), while the area will be a square metre. So, a Pa is actually a newton of force exerted uniformly over a square metre of area. Due to the force of gravity, a 1-kg mass develops a weight of just under 10N, so the pascal is quite a small pressure and normal atmospheric pressure is just over 100,000 Pa. This latter figure is called a 'bar' and is still far too large for normal met. usage. The millibar (a thousandth part of a bar) is the normal meteorological unit of pressure. In Europe this unit is called a hectopascal (hPa).

The SI system is a scientific system of units, but even it has its inconsistencies and sometimes important units in everyday use are excluded, e.g. the bar (b) and millibar (mb) are not truly SI. This is a reason for purists to call the millibar a hectopascal, which is an SI unit.

SIGNIFICANT WEATHER Weather which has significance for the activity in question. For example, charts produced for trans-Atlantic jets, etc. only show jetstreams and areas of deep cloud stuffed with cumulonimbus (see fig. S.2). These are, for them, significant pieces of weather and nothing else is of much importance except CAT (Clear Air Turbulence). Significant weather for gliders must include wind speed and direction, state of sky, chance of precipitation and its nature, etc; in other words, much more information is required by the glider pilot than by the jet pilot. Significant weather charts are produced especially on the fax output in the USA, but also on a day-to-day basis on European fax (see fig. S.2).

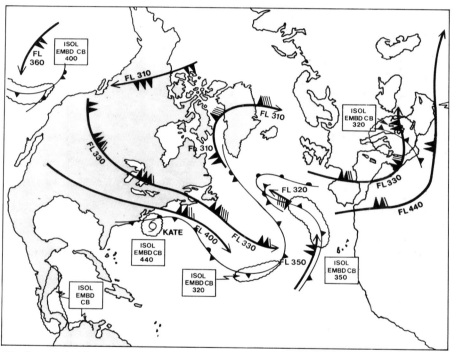

Fig. S.2 A significant weather chart for high altitude aviation. Jet streams and embedded Cb cloud are of most importance. Isol means isolated and the heights are levels or cloud tops in hundreds of feet

SLEET Mixture of rain and snow, and occurs when a warm layer exists near the ground so that falling snow partially melts on the way down.

SLOPE WINDS Occur when very cold air falls down steep mountain slopes, often under the impetus of a sympathetic isobaric gradient. Whenever flying under mountain peaks which are snow-capped, consider the danger of falling winds, especially if the falling wind should come across a constricting valley or fissure on its way down. These winds can appear without warning and are very dangerous to gliders and balloons. Extreme examples are the Mistral of the Gulf of Lions hinterland and the Bora of the Yugoslav side of the Adriatic Sea. Lesser slope winds will occur with the arrival over a massif of colder air, i.e. a cold

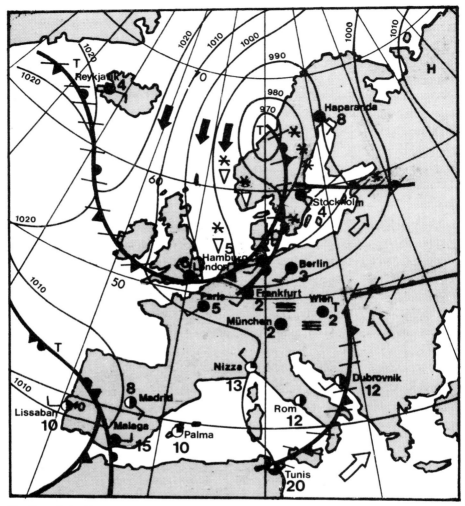

Fig. S.3 A significant weather chart as broadcast daily by Offenbach fax for the use of the press. Bold figures are expected temperatures and hatching indicates areas of extensive cloud

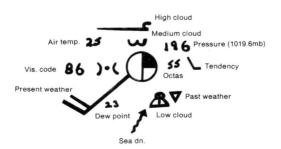

Fig. S.4 A station circle showing where the weather elements are plotted

front, whereas Föhn effects will be felt with warm air. Sometimes the slope wind will be due to thunderstorms or heavy showers over the heights and such winds have proved fatal to glider pilots on more than one occasion. Slope winds differ from katabatics only in their ferocity and the fact that a gradient wind in their direction aids them whereas the gentle katabatic appears most often when surface winds are calm.

SMOG Shortening of 'smoke fog': it is water fog contaminated by pollutants such as smoke or chemical products. It may also be used to describe haze due to sunlight reacting with exhaust and other fumes.

SNOW An infinitude of variations on the theme of a six-sided ice crystal. They say that no two snow flakes are alike, but who has managed to prove it? When a condensation nucleus such as a minute ice crystal finds itself in a wet super-cooled environment it grows rapidly, as water molecules have a direct affinity with the hexagonal shapes of the crystalline form of ice. By sheer chance, and because the environment is homogeneous, snow flakes grow six symmetrical fronds and so form a snow flake. These flakes often collide as they sink and form larger groups of flakes, and 'wet snow' is almost always like this.

The drier and colder the environment, the more likely it is that snow pellets will form. These are often called soft hail or graupel, and are white, opaque grains of ice with a diameter of between 2 and 5mm. At other times snow grains fall and this is often described, fairly accurately, as 'sago snow'.

In mountainous districts snow may appear out of nowhere, being blown ahead of the clouds in which it formed. The same explanation can be given for the times on the lowlands when it appears to snow from a clear sky.

SOARING Flight extended beyond the normal flight-path of the glider.

SPECIFIC HEAT Heat energy (joules) required to raise a kilogram of a substance by one degree Celsius. Water has by far the highest specific heat of any normal substance, which means it is slow to heat up and it also retains its heat. Thus the oceans become vast reservoirs of heat energy to fuel and modify the airmasses of the world. On the other hand, the solid substances of Earth have low specific heats, which means they warm up quickly and also lose heat quickly. Because of this, in the short term, it is considered that sea temperatures do not change while those of the land go through diurnal variation.

SQUALLS Defined as sudden increases in wind speed of at least 16 knots, with the mean speed rising to 22knots or more and lasting for at least a minute. However, to those who experience them a squall usually entails lashing rain to go with the wind increase.

STABILITY Refers to the tendency of an air parcel displaced upwards to sink back again. Warm air over cold air or ground surfaces is stable, but air which is stable on the lowlands may be forced into instability by ascent up hill and mountain slopes. Signs of stability include layer clouds, smoke which sinks after an initial rise, and heap clouds that become spread into layer clouds. Only dynamic lift will be present when stable conditions exist near the ground.

STALL Sudden loss of lift and increase in drag due to excessive angle of attack.

STATION CIRCLES Plotted on actual charts broadcast by weatherfax stations; an example is shown in fig. S.4. It is impossible and unnecessary from a practical point of view to give all the code symbols here, because the information that the glider pilot is likely to be interested in is mainly self-evident. In the example the wind is 20kt from SW and there is 2/8 cloud cover of a convective nature. There is some low cloud as well as medium and high cloud, but as the total amounts to only a quarter of the sky-dome covered there cannot be too much of any of it. See *Cloudiness*.

The visibility code is simple. Up to 50, just multiply by 100m, i.e. 31 = 3100m = 3.1km.

Figures 56–80 are read as kilometres by subtracting 50, i.e. $57 = 7$km, while $64 = 14$km.

It is evident from the example how the pressure is read and the tendency is a representation of the barograph trace, in this case falling, then steady. The air temperature and dewpoint temperature can be compared. When they are close to one another, fog or poor visibility is a possibility, especially if the observation was made, say, at 1800 or 2100Z (GMT).

There are various shades of meaning in the present and past weather symbols for which sight of the codes is needed to understand them fully, but even so the basic symbols will give an indication of what kind of weather is involved (see *Present weather*).

The precipitation symbols are increased in a group – up to four in diamond formation – as the intensity of the phenomenon becomes greater. Symbols in reversed brackets, as in the example, indicate that the precipitation is in sight but is not actually falling on the station.

Bad visibility is denoted by $=$ for mist and $\equiv$ for fog, while haze is represented by a chimney with a curl of smoke.

Ships indicate direction of sea as well as sea state, but these will not usually be of importance to glider pilots.

STORM As well as having its usual layperson's meaning, the term can include storm-force winds which have a mean speed of more than 47 knots, i.e. Force 10 on the Beaufort Scale.

STREAMLINES Indicate airflow, but unlike isobars they can be generated at a point, and they also disappear. They are used on charts to indicate airflow of winds in the tropics where the geostrophic force has become very slack and Buys Ballot's Law no longer applies. They are also lines along which Bernouille's Theorem applies in aerodynamic studies of both aerofoils and wind flow over and around obstacles.

SUBSIDENCE Technical term meaning the sinking of a body of air as a whole. It is pronounced 'sub-sid-ence'. When air sinks, it warms up at the same adiabatic rates as rising air cools. However, warming leads to evaporation of water droplets in clouds and so to their eventual disappearance. Thus the subsiding air over anticyclones and ridges of high pressure erodes high and medium cloud, often leaving extensive layers of low cloud in the strong subsidence inversion which results. Otherwise, the whole cloud mass may go to leave the clear skies popularly associated with highs but rarely experienced in Atlantic Europe. Strong subsidence inversions trap the surface layer of air and, if the sky is clear, very high temperatures and potentially dangerous explosive thermal conditions result. The height of the subsidence inversion can often be seen near sunset where the layer of surface obscuration cuts off into clearer air above. Subsidence inversions inhibit the growth of seabreezes, as the free convection required cannot take place.

SUPER ADIABATIC LAPSE RATES Occur near the ground on hot days. The surface temperature lapses at a rate greater than the DALR for some distance above the ground. It leads to 'explosive' convection and can be dangerous.

SUPERCELLS Very large Cb clouds without the multiple cell structure of lesser storms. See *Thunderstorms*.

SUPERCOOLING Natural state of water vapour and water droplets in clouds above the freezing level. When very pure, water does not freeze until well below the normal freezing point. It is possible for water to remain unfrozen to as low as -40°C. It is supercooled droplets that freeze on contact with aircraft surfaces to produce airframe icing.

SUPERSATURATION Also a natural state in the atmosphere and essential when cloud droplets and rain are formed. There has to be more water vapour available in the environment than is necessary to saturate it and the excess can then be converted into water.

SURFACE INVERSIONS Form near the ground on most nights when radiation occurs into clear skies.

SURFACE TEMPERATURE Recorded in a Stevenson Screen at 4ft (1.2m) above the ground.

SURFACE WIND Wind below 33ft (10m).

SYNOPTIC Term meaning 'over-view' and applied to weather charts which allow you to see at a glance the state of the weather.

TAIL WIND Wind blowing from behind you. Tail winds can quickly send gliders miles/ kilometres away from their launch sites and should be used only with caution.

TELL-TALES Pieces of yarn or cloth attached to a glider to show wind direction at take-off. They may also be used to show break-down in laminar flow over aerofoils.

TEMPERATURE Measure of the average energy of motion of the atoms or molecules in a substance. It has a natural zero – the Absolute Zero of Temperature – when all energy has been extracted from a substance and the atoms are inert. See *Kelvin Scale*.

A scale of temperature relies on the fact that certain physical attributes of known substances always occur at the same temperature, and these are accorded a number of degrees on the scale. The most important are the Ice Point (273.16K, 0°C or 32°F) and the Steam Point (373.16k, 100°C and 212°F). Ice Point is the temperature when a thermometer is placed in a mixture of ice and water, while steam point is found when pure water boils under a pressure of one Standard Atmosphere. For other points, both hotter and colder, consult a book of physical tables. Any impurities, such as salt, make the freezing point of water lower and so salt water will still be unfrozen even though the temperature is below Ice Point. Conversely, impurities make water boil at a higher temperature and so does increased atmospheric pressure. It follows that boiling water to make tea at a high altitude site will require less gas, as the water will boil at a temperature below 100°C.

The two standard domestic scales are Celsius and Fahrenheit; see *Celsius* for a conversion scale.

TENDENCY See *Barometric tendency*.

TEPHIGRAMS Thermodynamic diagrams that enable professional meteorologists to: assess cloud height and depth; estimate amount of cloud; see where frontal surfaces are; recognise airmasses (which may have lost most of their original surface characteristics by travelling a long way over land) from their upper air characteristics, etc.

Tephigrams (called Temps in fax broadcasts) are plotted twice a day following the simultaneous release all over the world of radiosonde balloons at midnight and midday GMT. It is the observations of temperature, humidity and pressure in the upper air from these ascents, coupled with the surface observations at the same time, which form the raw input to the computer models that forecast the isobaric and contour patterns for up to six days ahead.

The word 'tephigram' comes from the major coordinates used on the charts, which are temperature (T) against entropy (represented by the Greek letter phi (ϕ)). Entropy is a thermodynamic quantity whose meaning is often very difficult to grasp. In the context here lines of equal entropy are those along which air parcels, displaced in the vertical, will cool or warm at the DALR. These lines are called dry adiabatics, while the lines of equal temperature are isothermals. Thus on a graph, using coordinates of T against ϕ, dry adiabatics form a square grid with the isothermals and, as wet adiabatics and pressure levels can also be included on this complex chart, the state of the environment in which any parcel of air finds itself can be located. A simplified tephigram is shown in fig. T.1 on p.174.

The way any rising or sinking air parcel will change its characteristics is immediately

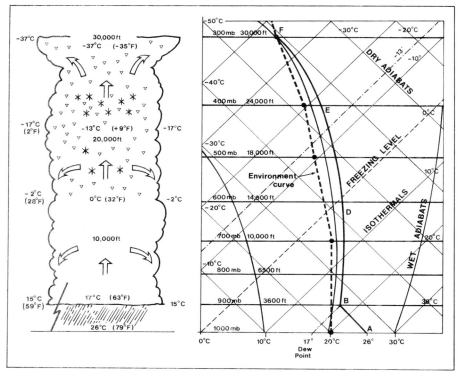

Fig. T.1   A simplified tephigram and the kind of Cb cloud which would have resulted from the conditions plotted on it

evident on the tephigram. For example, a thermal (whose temperature is 26°C at A) will move parallel to the dry adiabatics on the tephigram until it meets an isothermal line at the dewpoint (of 17°C at B). After this it moves (DEF) parallel to the wet adiabatics until it meets the (dashed) Environment curve (the air temperature measured by the radiosonde) at F. Now rising thermal and environmental air are at the same temperature and the thermal (after a brief overshoot) will stop rising.

In the example given, this was a day of thunderstorms, because the rising air (BDEF) did not meet the environment curve below the 300mb level. That means that the air did not stop rising below about 30,000ft when the temperature had fallen to about -36°C.

It will be noted that in order to accord with our natural inclinations the pressure lines are drawn horizontally, just as in the real atmosphere, which means the isothermals slope up SW to NE on the diagram while the dry adiabatics slope from SE to NW. Two useful isotherms are emphasised – the freezing level of 0°C and the -13°C isotherm above which rain-producing effects occur.

What the situation would be in the Cb cloud which resulted from this ascent of air is shown on the left. The updraught rises through the middle of the storm cell until its environment is populated by ice crystals and snowflakes. The latter initiate the rain process as they fall into warmer regions lower down.

In Britain the temps are broadcast on fax from Bracknell and are tephigrams, while on the Continent when they are broadcast from Offenbach they are Stuve Diagrams. The latter are pressure against temperature charts which do not have the same thermodynamic properties as the tephigram. They are, however, more easily understood by the layperson.

THERMAL LOWS Found over central parts of land masses during the middle of the day in unusually warm weather. They are most likely in the afternoons of summer, but can occur in spring and autumn. They need sluggish air of tropical origin and, when close enough to a coast to be fed by sea air, become the seats of heavy showers or thunderstorms.

THERMALS Form over land whenever the lowest air-deck is heated by the sun and the air is unstable. They are described fully in chapter 7.

THERMIC Term used in gliding circles to indicate those days when soaring in thermals is possible.

THUNDER Result of the sudden expansion of air heated to very high temperature along the path of a lightning flash. Thus whether it is seen or not, thunder indicates that a lightning flash must have occurred. Thunder rolls because of reverberations from the clouds on its way to the observer. Those who have been close to lightning flashes will tell you that the thunder is then one very loud sharp bang.

THUNDERSTORMS Can be understood once it is recognised that a 'thunderstorm' is the result of the birth, growth and decline of many individual storm cells. Individual storm cells can grow in mP airstreams (airmass thunderstorms) or are found embedded in frontal cloud masses when the winds are relatively strong. However, no cell can grow in an environment where there is considerable change in wind direction and/or speed through the middle reaches of the cells.

When the winds are sluggish and the air tropical in origin, as they can be in thermal lows and cols, then multicellular storms develop of the kind which are usually called 'a thunderstorm'. How these come about is evident from fig. T.2.

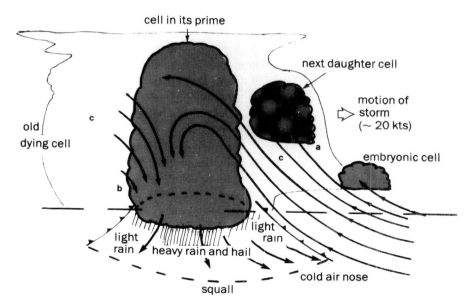

Fig. T.2 The stages in the growth and continuation of a thunderstorm. Daughter cells grow in the updraught drawn into the cell in its prime and also may be initiated in air being lifted over the cold air nose

A developed cell will produce strong downdraughts, due to the frictional effect of heavy rain and hail dragging cold upper air to the surface. This air pours out around the storm like pouring double cream onto a plate. The effect is to lift local warm air into instability. This creates a daughter cell which takes over the role of the parent as the latter dissipates. In this way a thunderstorm develops over a wide area, with cells in all stages of their life-cycle, from embryonic daughters through the mature hail stage to lifeless cells whose great anvil heads become pressed against the tropopause.

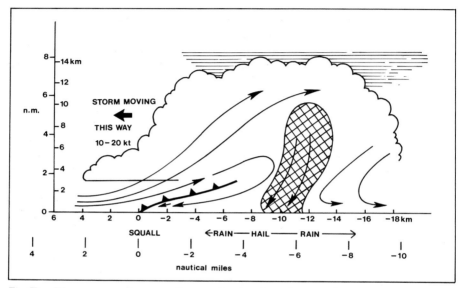

Fig. T.3   The anatomy of a supercell storm showing the main area of downdraughts

Three stages in the life cycle of a storm cell are shown in fig. T.2. In the developing stage (a) there is almost wholly rising air throughout the envelope of the cloud. However, as yet no rain has developed. In the mature stage (b) there are strong updraughts, especially at the leading edges, as well as very strong downdraughts in the body of the cloud. In this stage there is snow above the -8°C isotherm and ice crystals above the -25°C isotherm. Hail is formed when the rain drops are repeatedly lifted into cold upper regions by the angled updraught and fall to gain a coating of water before again being caught by the updraught. This process freezes layers of ice onto an embryonic drop so that it gains an onion-like skin.

In the dissipating stage there is only light rain; much of the air in the cell is sinking, but the upper reaches are still trying to rise and have to spread sideways to form the anvil-shaped tops which are the trademark of such storms. It is worth noting, however, that such anvil heads denote dying cells and it is only because daughters are growing alongside them that the storm keeps itself going.

The active life of a cell is about half an hour and only when the cells are in the most active mature (or hail) stage do they produce lightning and attendant thunder.

The fact that daughter cells grow around the edges of mature cells makes it a hazardous occupation trying to fly between what look like two separated cloud masses. In a short while that clear gap may become filled by a developing daughter cell.

There is a form of intense thunderstorm which can grow in strong wind shear (change of speed with height). This consists of a single immense cell called a 'supercell'. Supercells are bad storms that advance against the wind after a sultry calm. This wind is, as fig. T.3 shows, the warm inflow to the storm itself, leading to the old saying that 'thunderstorms come up against the wind'. Lesser cellular storms can also draw in air from ahead of them and so also come up against the wind when the surface winds are generally light. Any storm that does this is obviously highly active and is therefore likely to be a bad storm. Luckily, supercells are rare, but when they occur there may be hail of golf-ball size or bigger and smaller hail may grow inches deep on the ground. Flash floods may also occur in the lower reaches of high ground where the storm is active and vicious squalls from the direction of the storm come to replace the previous warm light inflow.

Cellular storms can move along paths that are conducive to their development. They may, for instance, seem to follow river valleys. This is due to the availability of moist air over these valleys so that daughter cells develop there in preference to elsewhere. This way the most active parts of a storm may 'crab' along the valley.

Cellular storms are not the only form of thunderstorm. There is a form of 'frontal' storm that generally develops over central France and moves up over the English Channel and neighbouring land areas. This form of storm (which is not confined to this area) develops in unstable middle reaches of the atmosphere so that most of the activity is occurring around 10,000ft. The lightning is most frequently from cloud to cloud (as the distance from cloud to ground is so large), giving rise to 'sheet' lightning and intensely rolling thunder. Such storms are also possible in mountainous districts when medium-level cloud, which would not be unstable over low ground, becomes lifted by having to flow over ridges and peaks. That such storms are possible is signalled by the onset of castellanus and floccus maybe hours before the actual outbreak of the high-level storm cells.

TIME OF DAY Usually given in the 24-hour clock where, for example, 1 p.m. becomes 1300 hours and 1.35 a.m. becomes 0135. The official met. day is based on GMT and is modified to take account of local time. Thus only in countries such as Britain and others which lie roughly on the Greenwich Meridian do clock times and GMT coincide – and then only when there is no Summer Time in force. Countries to the east of Britain have Zone Times which are ahead of GMT while those to the west lag on GMT. Eastern Standard Time in the US is GMT minus 5 hours, for example. Zone times are accorded

TABLE T.1 DATES AND TIMES OF SUNRISE AND SUNSET

Latitude	Location	Feb 18 and Oct 25	May 21 and Sep 23	Apr 21 and Aug 23	June 22
58N	North Scotland, Skaggerak, North Baltic	0730-9-1630	0600-12-1800	0445-14½-1915	0300-18-2100
52N	Southern Ireland, Holland, Central Southern England, Poland	0700-10-1700	0600-12-1800	0600-14-1900	0345-16½-2015
46N	Central Biscay coast of France, North Adriatic	0656-10½-1715	0600-12-1800	0600-14-1900	0400-16-2000
38N	Lisbon, Toe of Italy, Southern Aegean	0630-11-1730	0600-12-1800	1515-13½-1845	0430-15-1930

letters; GMT is Z while British Summer Time, being one hour ahead of GMT, is A. A country whose standard clock time is 2 hours ahead of GMT will be B, and so on, round the world.

From a gliding point of view the only viable hours are those of daylight and those for soaring will be confined to when thermals can occur. The length of daylight and the rough times of sunrise and sunset can be gauged from table T.1 for four representative latitudes.

As the sun needs time to heat the ground, the times between which thermic conditions can exist can be determined.

TORNADOES Locally intense whirls of air induced by excessive instability. They usually form in association with Cb clouds. The latter may be individual storm areas or may be embedded in sharp, cold frontal cloud. The tornadoes of the mid United States are the most devastating and some of the facts about their effects seem almost unbelievable. Britain and Europe generally experience many more tornadoes than is generally believed. One cold front moving down from the north-west across central England was responsible for upward of a hundred small tornadoes and that was only detected by Michael Hunt of Anglia TV asking for reports from viewers. Many more tornadoes go unreported or maybe do not even develop sufficiently to produce more than a few local remarks.

The tornadoes will start with a funnel-cloud hanging below a passing Cb cloud and will then extend downwards towards the ground. The winds usually rotate anti-clockwise in the Northern Hemisphere and may get to a hundred knots in the most severe cases. In Britain they are mainly products of autumn and winter when the sea temperatures are at their highest. However, they are not restricted to daylight hours and can suddenly appear during the night, being particularly devastating to caravans, tents, etc.

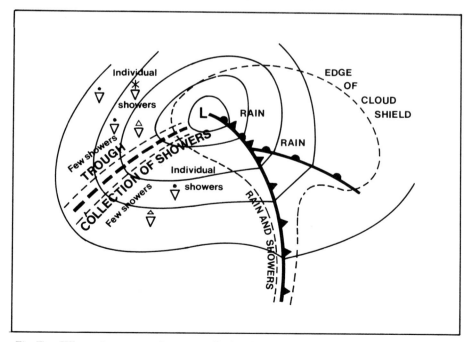

Fig. T.4 Where airmass troughs are usually found. There are frontal troughs along the fronts which are deeper where the isobars kink the most

TROPICAL CYCLONES Severe forms of depression that form over warm sub-tropical waters and migrate – often on roughly parabolic paths – to cooler climes. Those of the North Atlantic are hurricanes, of the China Sea, typhoons, and on the north coast of Australia, Willy Willies.

TROPOPAUSE Atmospheric boundary between the troposphere and the stratosphere. It is more or less an isothermal layer which confines weather processes below it.

TROPOSHERE Air-deck below the tropopause where all the important weather processes occur.

TROUGHS Regions where the isobars are 'v' shaped towards higher pressure and in these regions whatever weather there is will tend to worsen (see fig. T.4).

Troughs tend to be of two kinds: frontal and airmass. The frontal trough is evident on weather maps when the isobars kink across a front. Often the wind shift is a right angle or more, and occasionally, when a front is slow-moving, the wind shift may be nearly as large as two right angles. In these cases, however, the transition is not likely to be at all sharp and a zone of transition will exist which may take hours to pass, or the front may become quasi-stationary, in which case it can persist for days.

Airmass troughs will exist in most cyclonic airstreams. They tend to rotate round the periphery of low centres, like the spokes of a wheel. They may be noted as periods when, under the cloud shield of a low, the weather deteriorates for a time. What was a relatively dry period is followed by lowering cloud and rain (or other precipitation) or showers will break out. At other times fair weather becomes temporarily invaded by a build-up of cloud. This can be at high altitude, due to an upper trough whose effects do not penetrate to ground level. Then the weather improves for a while. Cloud lifts and may even break before another trough swings in. Such troughs demand a low which is not moving very much, but whose centre is not all that far away.

In mP airstreams the airmass trough is a well-known beast, visually resembling a cold front but with no change of airmass across it. Usually there is a build-up across the wind of Cb with interspersed layer clouds. It normally takes something like an hour to pass before the weather reverts to typical mP type, but maybe with very little heap cloud for some time afterwards.

TURBULENCE Means by which the smooth flow of an airstream is disturbed. It can be either mechanical or thermal.

Mechanical turbulence is almost always present in the wind during the day, although it may die out to near laminar flow in the evening or after dark. It is due to collision of the wind with surface obstacles and typically has a period of a few seconds. However, much larger, turbulent eddies are induced in stable airstreams when the wind speed grows towards gale force.

Thermal turbulence is contributed by the rising and sinking currents around thermals or similar convective entities and this has a period measured in minutes. The mechanical turbulence may mask the thermal turbulence features, especially during the mornings of days which are partially unstable, i.e. cumulus days.

UNSTABLE When displaced upwards, an air parcel continues to rise of its own accord. However, the air may be unstable to great heights or only to a limited height. It may be unstable in the middle levels (alto cloud levels) and not near the ground. Air which is close to being unstable over lowlands may become unstable when forced to rise up slopes. This is called conditional instability, because it depends on the conditions under which the air will become unstable.

UPPER WINDS Tend to be stronger than surface winds and to be less complex, as they are mainly free of the surface. Unlike surface winds which blow to keep Low Pressure on their Left, upper winds blow to keep Low Temperature on their Left. The upper wester-lies form series of immense waves whose motion and wavelength have a profound effect on the motion and formation of surface pressure features. Their actual trajectories are to be found on the contour charts for the standard pressure levels as well as on significant weather charts for aviation.

UPWIND Direction looking into the wind. It is not necessarily the direction from which a change in the weather will come, as when weather is changing the upper winds are crossed to the surface winds (see *Crossed winds' rules*). Also, low clouds will normally come from a direction to the right of what appears to be upwind to the surface observer. Cloud movement should always be assessed to gain an idea of what changes, if any, there are between the wind near the surface and that at the altitude you hope to reach.

VALLEY WINDS Blow up valleys when the sun heats mountain slopes.

VARIOMETERS Detect rate of climb or descent through small changes in air pressure. As the glider sinks through the surrounding air, the variometer detects whether this air is rising or sinking and is essential when seeking thermal lift. Modern electronic versions give an audio output, which rises in intensity as the rate of climb increases, as well as an analogue read-out.

VEER Wind veers when it shifts its direction clockwise. Winds veer across almost all fronts in the Northern Hemisphere.

VISIBILITY How far the unaided eye can detect the form of objects. This distance is greater than for unlit objects; the subject is covered in chapter 13.

WARM FRONTS Zones of transition between cold or cool air and warmer air. The most likely airmasses involved are mP ahead and mT behind the front. However, other forms of airmass may be involved (see chapter 3).

WARM SECTOR 'V'-shaped wedge of warm air that lies between the cold and warm fronts of a typical depression. At its purest, the weather in warm sectors is muggy, with much cloud at all levels. There is high relative humidity and so cloud forms on windward coasts and slopes, and may get thick enough to produce drizzle or even light rain. There is an ever-present risk of fog or low stratus which will not exist in an airstream of polar origin.

Warm airmasses can dry out with time and can lead to days with high temperatures and sometimes to thunderstorms. The outlook is that this warm air must at some time be swept away by the arrival of a cold front.

WATER SPOUTS Funnel clouds formed over the sea which may occasionally invade coastal cliff sites. They often are just tubes of spray, but the winds in them are strong and should not be taken lightly. At times they can be seen in the English Channel, but are much more prevalent towards and into the Mediterranean. They usually demand a Cb cloud, but in the Mediterranean they are sometimes seen apparently stretching up into blue sky.

A more dangerous form is the tornado storm spout which may be encountered in southern latitudes where a tornado has invaded a water area and sucked up a great deal of water.

WAVE DEPRESSIONS Prevalent when a cold front trails back across a region from a depression that has passed and lies somewhere to the north-east. They are best visualised as the kind of waves that can be flicked into a rope when one end has been tied, say, to the handle of a door. The rope represents the cold front and the wave is a low pressure region which never really develops, but runs quickly along the front just as the wave runs along the rope (see fig. W.1).

Waves slow up the clearance of cold fronts. Sometimes they make their presence felt

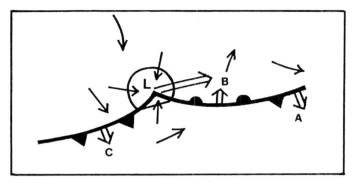

Fig. W.1   The motion of a frontal wave. The front at A is moving as we would expect, and an observer at B should see a clearance coming. However, the wave motion makes the front move back and the clearance disappears. Only later, when the wave has tracked by, does the front move the right way and the clearance comes. Winds, it will be noticed, close to the centre blow straight into it

when a clearance comes on the windward horizon, disappears and then the rain begins again. When that happens a wave is certainly responsible and you will have to wait for perhaps another few hours before the cold front can again move down over you and bring a true clearance.

In winter, waves can bring a considerable accumulation of snow to add to the snow which the cold front itself has brought.

WEATHER SYSTEMS Features which isobars indicate on the weather map. They include depressions, tropical cyclones, troughs, highs, ridges and cols.

WIND Air in motion; many of its aspects are covered in Part 1. To change speed from one set of units to another the following conversion figures are used:

$$\text{1 knot} = \text{0.514 m/s} = \text{1.15 mph} = \text{1.852 km/hr.}$$

WIND CHILL Effect of wind speed on the sensation value of temperature. Because the body loses heat by evaporation from its pores, and this process is enhanced by wind speed,

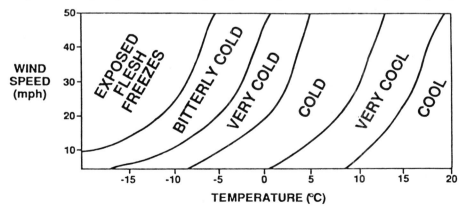

Fig. W.2   The degree of wind chill can be gauged from this diagram. Assess your maximum penetration speed and the temperature at the height you expect to reach and read off what it will feel like

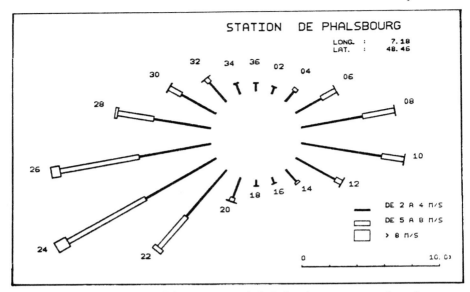

Fig. W.3 A typical wind rose. The percentage winds (using the percentage scale at the bottom) from, say, 080 degrees are 5% between 2 and 4 m/s; 3% between 5 and 8 m/s; and very few above 8 m/s

so the body will always lose more heat when exposed to a wind than in still air. Wind chill is an important factor in gliding where temperature usually falls with height at the same time as penetrating the air must provide a relative wind, whatever the actual wind is doing. How to assess wind chill is shown in fig. W.2.

WIND ROSES Useful to give an idea of the chances of getting wind from a certain direction and of a certain speed. The one illustrated (see fig. W.3) is for Phalsbourg, a town in France in the Department of Moselle, and stands on a thousand-foot (300m) plateau between Saverne and Nancy. Averages of the wind speed and direction for, in this case, 21 years are plotted at 20° intervals and show that SW is the most likely direction, with very few winds from either N or S. Reading the 240° example we have 6% between 2 and 4 m/s (4-8 knots); 7% between 5 and 8 m/s (10-16 knots); and 1% of stronger winds.

When examining wind roses and making inferences from them, you have to be very careful. This one looks as if the anemometer lies in an east-west valley and therefore it may not apply to where you expect to fly. You may use such roses as a guide, and in flattish country they may be a good guide, but the wind statistics may be quite different at nearby sites in the mountains.

WIND SHEAR Change in wind speed, with distance measured across the wind. Wind may shear both in the vertical and the horizontal plane, but the former is of greatest importance to pilots taking off and landing.

WIND SOCK Important piece of auxiliary equipment for the glider pilot, as it is large enough to be seen from altitude and so indicates any major changes in the wind direction at the take-off site. It is also light, unbreakable and simple to transport.

WINDWARD Direction facing into the wind. Its opposite is leeward.

WING LOADING Weight-to-area ratio of a glider; found by dividing the all-up flying weight by the wing area.

BIBLIOGRAPHY AND FURTHER READING

ABC of Paragliding, Aupetit (Editions, Retine, 1986)
The Complete Hang Gliding Guide, Whittal (A & C Black, 1984)
The Complete Microlight Guide, Welch (A & C Black, 1983)
The Complete Soaring Guide, Welch (A & C Black, 1986)
Flying Conditions, Pagen (Denis Pagen, USA, 1990)
Hang Gliding Techniques, Pagen (Denis Pagen, USA, 1982)
Meteorology and Flight, Bradbury (A & C Black, 1989)
Paragliding Flight, Pagen (Denis Pagen, USA, 1990)
Reading the Weather, Watts (Adlard Coles, 1987)
Skywings magazine, Williams (Trefenter, Aberystwyth, Dyfed)
Soaring Hang Gliders, Welch and Hill (John Murray, 1981)
Wind and Sailing Boats, Watts (David & Charles, 1973)
Understanding Flying Weather, Piggott (A & C Black, 1988)
Understanding Gliding, Piggott (A & C Black, 1977)

INDEX